PRENTICE HALL

Teacher's Guide

FORENSIC SCIENCE

PEARSON

Boston, Massachusetts
Chandler, Arizona
Glenview, Illinois
Shoreview, Minnesota
Upper Saddle River, New Jersey

PRENTICE HALL

Forensic Science

Resources

- Student Edition
- Teacher's Guide
- Student Handbook
- Student Handbook, Annotated Teacher's Edition
- Chapter and Unit Tests
- Forensic Science Videos
- Materials Kits

13-digit ISBN 978-0-13-362747-3

10-digit ISBN 0-13-362747-0

PEARSON

2 3 4 5 6 7 8 9 10 12 11 10 09 08

Contents

Inquiry Skills Charts

Forensic Science provides many opportunities for students to think like a scientist—to ask questions and to search for answers. The program provides comprehensive teaching, practice, and assessment of science skills, with an emphasis on the process skills necessary for inquiry. In the student text, there are the following types of activities: Discover Activity, Skills Activity, Math Analyzing Data, At-Home Activity, and You Be the Judge. There is also one Skills Lab per chapter. In the Student Handbook, there are worksheets for the Skills Labs, plus instructions and worksheets for eleven Lab Investigations and four Chapter Projects. The charts list the skills addressed in the program and cite locations where each skill is used.

Basic Process Skills			
	Student Text: Activities	**Student Text: Caption and Assessment Questions**	**Student Text and Student Handbook: Labs and Chapter Projects**
Observing	7, 19, 24, 98	18, 41, 75, 117	Skills Labs 1, 2 Lab Investigations 1, 5–10 Chapter Projects 1–3
Inferring	83, 96, 126	8, 38, 41, 47, 71, 81, 85, 99, 110, 112, 128, 131	Skills Lab 1 Lab Investigations 7, 9 Chapter Projects 1, 3, 4
Predicting	80, 83, 87, 126	30, 31, 33, 41, 71, 79, 103, 120	
Classifying	63, 79	21, 71, 79, 112, 131	Skills Lab 2 Lab Investigations 3, 5, 6, 8 Chapter Project 2
Making Models	58, 64, 66, 120		Skills Lab 4 Lab Investigations 1, 4, 9 Chapter Projects 1, 4
Communicating	13, 68, 79, 85, 112	31, 40, 51, 70, 99, 102, 128, 130	Skills Labs 1–4 Lab Investigations 1–11 Chapter Project 4
Measuring	21, 87		Skills Labs 2–4 Lab Investigations 1, 2, 6, 9
Calculating	16, 20, 34, 38, 48, 83, 115, 126	38, 41, 95, 103, 131	Skills Labs 2–4 Lab Investigation 6
Creating Data Tables			Skills Lab 2 Lab Investigations 1, 2, 9, 10 Chapter Projects 1, 2, 4
Graphing	23		Chapter Project 2

Advanced Process Skills

	Student Text: Activities	Student Text: Caption and Assessment Questions	Student Text and Student Handbook: Labs and Chapter Projects
Posing Questions	119, 124	41, 120	Lab Investigation 2 Chapter Projects 1, 4
Developing Hypotheses	34, 54, 74, 106	13, 125	Skills Lab 1 Chapter Project 4
Designing Experiments			Skills Labs 2–4
Controlling Variables	26		Lab Investigations 3, 4, 6 Chapter Projects 2, 3
Forming Operational Definitions	44		Lab Investigation 5
Interpreting Data	34, 82, 83, 88	9, 36, 71, 82, 103	Skills Labs 1–3 Lab Investigations 5, 8, 11 Chapter Projects 2, 3
Drawing Conclusions	32, 47, 48, 90	38, 67, 71, 85, 103, 128, 131	Skills Labs 2, 3 Lab Investigations 4–7, 9, 10 Chapter Projects 3, 4

Critical Thinking Skills

	Student Text: Activities	Student Text: Caption and Assessment Questions	Student Text and Student Handbook: Labs and Chapter Projects
Comparing and Contrasting	48, 123	13, 28, 38, 41, 45, 51, 56, 68, 71, 85, 97, 99, 103, 131	Skills Labs 2, 4 Lab Investigation 2, 6–10 Chapter Project 2
Applying Concepts	63, 123	13, 31, 35, 38, 41, 51, 55, 58, 61, 71, 84, 85, 90, 94, 95, 103, 109, 112, 116, 127, 128	Chapter Projects 1, 4
Interpreting Photographs	19	26, 49, 50	Lab Investigations 1, 2 Chapter Project 2
Interpreting Graphs, Diagrams, and Maps	23, 34, 48, 126	60, 65, 89, 92, 93, 103, 114, 118, 119, 131	Chapter Project 1
Relating Cause and Effect		31, 41, 46, 71, 85, 95, 103, 131	Lab Investigations 3, 9
Making Generalizations	87	31, 38, 51, 61, 68, 79, 112	Lab Investigation 5
Making Judgments	6, 63, 111, 113, 123	11, 21, 31, 51, 61, 99	Lab Investigation 11 Chapter Project 4
Problem Solving	23	21, 31, 41, 71, 75, 95, 103	Lab Investigation 2
Sequencing		13, 68, 79, 95	Chapter Project 1

Master Materials List

Forensic Science offers a range of activities in the student text. Some are minds-on. Others use simple materials, which are listed in the charts below. You can use the charts to help you plan your activities and order supplies. The materials listed in the consumable and nonconsumable charts are available from Science Kit. They can be ordered at www.sciencekit.com, or by calling 800-828-7777. See the Student Handbook, Annotated Teacher's Edition for additional Labs and a listing of the materials required for those activities.

Consumable Materials			
Description	**Activity**	**Team Size**	**Quantity per Class**
Anti-A serum, fake	CP 3	small group	1 bottle
Anti-B serum, fake	CP 3	small group	1 bottle
balloons, small	DIS 2-3	small group	5–6
blood, fake, for blood spatter	DIS 3-2	small group	5–6 15-mL bottles
blood, fake, for blood typing	CP 3	small group	1 set of 4 bottles
clay	SA 2-3	pair	15 oz/450 g
filter paper, 15-cm, medium flow	CP 2	small group	12 pieces
food coloring, three colors	SA 2-2	individual	1 bottle each
ink pads with washable ink	SA 3-1	pair	2–3
ink, black, washable	CP 2 SL 2	small group individual	600–720 mL 240–360 mL
markers, washable	DIS 3-1	individual	6
markers, dry erase	SL 2	individual	15
pads, felt	CP 2 SL 2	small group individual	5–6 2–3
paper, graph	CP 2, SL 4	small group	20 sheets
pens, black water-soluble ink	CP 2	small group	3 brands
poster board	CP 4	small group	5–6 sheets
sand, coarse	DIS 2-2	pair	15 oz/450 g
straws, wide, plastic	SA 2-3	pair	15
transparency grids	SL 2	individual	30
wood, soft	SA 2-1	pair	2–6 strips

ACTIVITY KEY

CP: Chapter Project **DIS:** Discover Activity **SA:** Skills Activity **SL:** Skills Lab

Nonconsumable Materials			
Description	**Activity**	**Team Size**	**Quantity per Class**
funnels	DIS 2-3	small group	5–6
graduated cylinders	CP 2	small group	5–6
hand lenses	CP 3 DIS 2-2 DIS 3-1, DIS 3-4, DIS 4-3	small group pair individual	5–6 15 30
protractors	SL 3	individual	30
rulers, metric, 15-cm	CP 2, DIS 3-2, SL 4 SL 2, SL 3	small group individual	5–6 30
snap cubes, three colors	DIS 3-3	individual	90 each
spray bottles	CP 2	small group	5–6
tire tread sections	CP 2	small group	5–6
trays, blood-typing	CP 3	small group	5–6
trays, plastic	CP 2 SL 2	small group individual	5–6 2–3

Additional Materials			
Description	**Activity**	**Team Size**	**Quantity per Class**
bar codes	SA 3-3	pair	10–12
cardboard	SL 4	small group	10–12 pieces
cornstarch	DIS 2-3	small group	5–6 tsp
cotton swabs	SA 2-2 SA 2-3	individual pair	33 15
cups, foam	SA 2-2	individual	33
cups, small plastic	CP 2	small group	5–6
facial tissues	DIS 3-1	individual	30
glue, white	SA 2-2	individual	4–8 drops
newspapers	CP 2 SL 2	small group individual	5–6 2–3
objects, small	SA 1-1, DIS 1-4	individual	6–10
paper, tracing	SL 3	individual	30 sheets
pins	DIS 2-3 SA 2-3	small group pair	5–6 15
recording of voices	SA 3-4	class	1
signatures, multiple	DIS 3-4	individual	30 copies
spoons, plastic	DIS 2-3	small group	5–6
stopwatches or clock	CP 2, CP 3	small group	5–6
tape, transparent	SL 2 SL 4	individual small group	2 rolls 5 rolls
tools, three types	SA 2-1	pair	1 each
toothpicks	CP 3	small group	10–12

Pacing Options

Forensic Science lends itself to many different pacing options. You can teach all four chapters as a unit. Or you can teach Chapter 1 at the beginning of the year to introduce or reinforce inquiry skills and schedule subsequent chapters to coincide with specific curriculum needs. For example, Chapter 2 can be used to help teach properties of matter and Chapter 3 can be used to help teach a unit on cells. You might want to save Chapter 4 until after students have completed the appropriate social studies content, especially if you plan to teach the chapter with a colleague.

Pacing Chart

	Periods	Blocks
UNIT PROJECT: The Missing Masterpiece	ongoing	ongoing
CHAPTER 1 Crime Scene Investigation		
1 Using Science to Solve Crimes	3–4	1½–2
2 Securing and Recording a Crime Scene	2–3	1–1½
FORENSICS & EARTH SCIENCE: Mapping Crime	1	½
3 Types of Evidence	2–3	1–1½
4 Collecting Physical Evidence	2	1
Chapter 1 Review and Assessment	1	½
CHAPTER 2 Prints and Trace Evidence		
1 Prints	3–4	1½–2
2 Trace Evidence	3–4	1½–2
FORENSICS & PHYSICAL SCIENCE: Arson Investigations	1	½
3 Identifying Firearms	2	1
Chapter 2 Review and Assessment	1	½
CHAPTER 3 Identifying an Individual		
1 Fingerprints	4	2
2 Evidence From Blood	3	1½
FORENSICS & LIFE SCIENCE: Facial Reconstruction	1	½
3 DNA Evidence	4–5	2–2½
4 Handwriting and Voice Identification	2	1
Chapter 3 Review and Assessment	1	½
CHAPTER 4 Bringing Evidence to Court		
1 From Arrest to Trial	3	1½
2 Presenting Evidence in a Trial	3	1½
FORENSICS & TECHNOLOGY: Modeling a Crime Scene	1	½
3 The Final Stages of a Trial	2	1
Chapter 4 Review and Assessment	1	½

INTRODUCTION TO UNIT PROJECT

An ancient Chinese proverb states, "I hear, I forget; I see, I remember; I do, I understand." What better way for students to understand the concepts of forensic science than by doing activities to solve a mystery as they study the lessons? The activities provide students with hands-on opportunities to apply science process skills and forensic science techniques.

The Missing Masterpiece

You have two options. The first option is to use the Missing Masterpiece mystery, which is described in the student text and supported in the Teacher's Guide and Student Handbook. This option does not require you to set up a crime scene. The second option is to use the suggestions on pages 2–3 to plan a mystery at your school. This option requires that you set up a simulated crime scene.

Chapter 1

Investigating a Crime Scene

Teams observe the crime scene and make inferences about what happened. Teams also describe how to secure the crime scene, sketch the crime scene, prepare questions for an eyewitness, and identify physical evidence.

TEACHING TIP Divide the class into five or six teams. Explain that members of each team will work together to solve the mystery and present the case. Reinforce the concept that most forensic investigations and legal proceedings rely on teamwork.

Chapter 2

Analyzing Print and Trace Evidence

In Part 1, teams identify tire brands by comparing tire prints to a database of tire tread photographs. In Part 2, teams use paper chromatography to analyze ink isolated from a note found at the crime scene. Using their results, teams identify the brand of pen used to write the note. By the end of both parts, students have narrowed the list of suspects from 36 to 4.

Chapter 3

Identifying the Thief

In this activity, teams identify the thief by using ABO blood typing to analyze fake blood found at the crime scene.

Chapter 4

Conducting a Trial

In Part 1, teams prepare visual exhibits for presentation during a mock trial. In Part 2, students assume the roles of various trial court personnel and present the case to a jury of their classmates. You may want to consider team-teaching this activity, and perhaps all of Chapter 4, with a social studies teacher.

Alternative Crime Scene

These guidelines are designed to help you set up your own crime scene and still take advantage of the activity worksheets in the Student Handbook. Even if you decide not to set up your own crime scene the first year, you may want to consider this approach in subsequent years.

Deciding on a Crime

When deciding on the crime that will be the basis of your mystery, select something appropriate for your classes. Keep in mind that some students may have experienced trauma from actual crimes. So deciding on a crime that is too realistic might not be appropriate. What you need is a crime that is engaging but not too serious. For example, you might decide that a prominent object in the classroom or school has been stolen. If so, select an object that can be removed for several days, such as a class skeleton, a school mascot, or a sports trophy.

Locating the Crime Scene

Choose a location for your crime scene that can remain undisturbed for several days. Set up the crime scene at a time when students are not in school. Alert the cleaning crew not to clean up the area where your crime scene is located. If you use fake blood as evidence in your crime scene, alert your administration and janitorial department before setting up the scene.

Enlisting Help From Your Colleagues

One of the challenges of setting up your own mystery is convincing your colleagues to act as the perpetrator (perp) and other suspects. Administrators and other faculty might be reluctant the first year. But after they see what you are trying to accomplish and how enthusiastic your students are about solving the mystery, your colleagues will be eager to participate in subsequent years.

The perp must be willing to donate evidence, such as hair samples, and perhaps place fingerprints on objects that will be found at the crime scene. Be sure to make up a motive for your perp. Also fabricate a story about his or her whereabouts at the time of the crime. Other suspects must be willing to be fingerprinted, interviewed, and provide hair samples (or whatever evidence you decide to include).

Take mug shots of all suspects and post the photos on a bulletin board. Leave room beneath each photo for students to list facts and the results of analyzing evidence. If your scenario includes students questioning suspects, instruct the innocent suspects to tell the truth during their interviews. They do not have to make up any stories. Only the perp will need to lie.

Pacing

The major issue you have to decide is whether to do all the mystery activities at once, or spread out the activities over the length of the unit. If you decide to spread out the activities, keep in mind that the crime scene needs to remain intact until evidence is collected from it. You will also need to decide whether to do some of the activities before teaching the related content in class.

Deciding on Evidence

When deciding what evidence to use in your scenario, consider selecting evidence that can be analyzed using the worksheets in the Student Handbook. Refer to the table for examples of evidence that relate to the existing activities.

You will probably want to plant evidence on each suspect's desk. Tell students that they need to confine their searches for evidence to the areas that you designate. The planted evidence should correspond to the evidence at the crime scene. For example, if shoe prints are included in the crime scene, then the suspects will need shoes with different tread designs. You might also consider throwing in some "red herrings" to make solving the mystery more challenging.

You should also plant some clues related to the motive for the crime. For example, if a school mascot bear was stolen, you might plant books about bears as evidence. You might also leave a note from the perp at the crime scene that suggests the motive for the crime.

Suggestions for Evidence to Use

Evidence	Student Handbook Activity
Shoe print made from ink, dirt, fake blood, or flour	Chapter 2 Skills Lab
Water-based ink on a note for paper chromatography of ink	Chapter 2 Project
Tire prints to compare with a tire tread photo database	Chapter 2 Project
Tire impressions to make tire casts	Lab Investigation 4
Hair samples from suspects, a dog, and other sources	Lab Investigation 5
A smudge of lipstick on the rim of a glass for paper chromatography of lipstick	Lab Investigation 6
Wire that has been cut by various tools	Lab Investigation 7
Drops of fake blood for ABO blood testing	Chapter 3 Project
Handwritten note for handwriting analysis	Chapter 3 Skills Lab
Fingerprints, such as latent prints on a glass, ink prints on a note, or bloody fingerprints on a tool	Lab Investigation 8
Fake blood spatter patterns	Lab Investigation 9
Partially eaten piece of candy for DNA analysis	Lab Investigation 10

Teaching Tips

Have students prepare a list of questions to use when interviewing suspects. Require that students come to you with the results of their interviews. They must convince you to issue a search warrant for a suspect's designated area.

If you do not want to do the DNA electrophoresis activity (Lab Investigation 10 in the Student Handbook), you can use bar codes to simulate DNA testing results. Teams can compare bar codes that represent DNA profiles from the suspects with bar codes that represent a DNA profile made from crime scene evidence.

Chapter 1

Crime Scene Investigation

Chapter at a Glance SE pp. 4–41

Resources

Project Investigating a Crime Scene

- Chapter Project Worksheet

Lesson 1

Using Science to Solve Crimes

1.1.1 Identify inquiry skills used to solve crimes.
1.1.2 Explain the importance of teamwork in solving crimes.
1.1.3 Compare methods used to solve crimes today with those used in the past.

- Vocabulary Worksheet
- Reading and Note Taking Guide 1-1
- Skills Lab Worksheet
- Video Viewing Guide 1
- Video: Clues From a Murder
- Video: The Mysterious Ice Man

Lesson 2

Securing and Recording a Crime Scene

1.2.1 Describe how to secure a crime scene.
1.2.2 Identify methods investigators use to record a crime scene.

- Reading and Note Taking Guide 1-2
- Laboratory Investigation 1: Recording a Crime Scene

Forensics & Earth Science
Mapping Crime

- SciLinks: longitude

Lesson 3

Types of Evidence

1.3.1 Describe the benefits and drawbacks of direct evidence.
1.3.2 Compare the methods used to help witnesses identify suspects.
1.3.3 Explain why physical evidence is key to solving crimes.

- Reading and Note Taking Guide 1-3
- Laboratory Investigation 2: Making Faces
- Video: Interviewing Witnesses

Lesson 4

Collecting Physical Evidence

1.4.1 Identify factors investigators consider before searching a crime scene.
1.4.2 Describe methods investigators use to ensure that the evidence found at a crime scene can be used in court.
1.4.3 Explain how investigators protect themselves at a crime scene.

- Reading and Note Taking Guide 1-4
- Laboratory Investigation 3: Collecting Physical Evidence
- SciLinks: careers in science

Review and Assessment

- Chapter 1 Test

Chapter Activities Planner

Activity/Time	Inquiry	Team Size/Materials	Skills
Chapter Project Ongoing, 2 weeks	Open-ended	Team Size: small group Illustration on SE p. 1	observing, measuring, posing questions, communicating
Lesson 1			
Discover Activity 10 minutes	Guided	Team Size: pair	making judgments
Skills Activity 15 minutes	Directed	Team Size: individual items such as a pencil stub with tooth marks, a marble, a gum wrapper, a colored paper clip, and a refrigerator magnet	observing
Skills Lab 20 minutes	Directed	Team Size: pair	observing, inferring, developing hypotheses
Lesson 2			
Discover Activity 20 minutes	Guided	Team Size: individual	calculating
Skills Activity 10 minutes	Guided	Team Size: individual Figure 9, SE pp. 18–19	observing
Skills Activity 10 minutes	Directed	Team Size: individual	calculating
At-Home Activity 40 minutes	Open-ended	Team Size: small group measuring tape, large unlined white paper or graph paper	observing, measuring
Lesson 3			
Discover Activity 15 minutes	Guided	Team Size: individual an unfamiliar person	observing
Skills Activity 10 minutes	Guided	Team Size: pair	controlling variables
Lesson 4			
Discover Activity 20 minutes	Guided	Team Size: individual items such as hairs, soil, broken glass, chewed gum, a few drops of fake blood	drawing conclusions

Chapter 1 Crime Scene Investigation

From the Author

Most students are fascinated by crime scene investigations. If they are avid watchers of television crime shows, your students are likely to have a number of misconceptions about forensic science. They may think, for example, that investigators are able to solve every crime that is reported or that most crimes are solved in a few days. Students may also think that forensic scientists are responsible for interviewing witnesses and interrogating suspects.

It is easy for students (and adults) to be so impressed by the modern technology used by forensic scientists that they ignore the most important tool available for solving crimes—the human mind. The habits of mind that investigators relied on hundreds of years ago—observing, inferring, predicting, and so on—are still key to solving crimes today.

Crime can be a sensitive issue for students who have been victims of crimes, who live in neighborhoods with higher than average crime rates, or who have family members who have been convicted of crimes. Never ask students to disclose information they would rather keep confidential, and always give them other options for activities in which they are asked to apply what they learn to their own lives.

Background

FIRST RESPONDERS The first people who respond to a crime scene take note of persons or vehicles leaving the area. They look for victims and suspects. They identify dangers, such as an agitated dog guarding a body, that need to be addressed before other investigators respond. The first responders will usually secure the core area—the part of the crime scene where most of the evidence is concentrated. They will also record the original location of a victim or an object that is moved and share this information when other investigators arrive.

CRIME SCENE INVESTIGATORS Students who do research on crime scene investigations are likely to see different titles used to describe the same job. For example, the person who collects evidence at a crime scene may be called an evidence technician, an evidence recovery technician, a crime scene technician, or a field evidence technician. The titles may vary, but one thing remains constant: A crime scene investigator gets only one chance to perform a thorough, untainted search.

When a CSI arrives at a crime scene, he or she will block off an area larger than the core area. The CSI will talk with the first responders to find out whether they had to disturb the scene in any way. The CSI will also gather information that might be helpful in determining a plan of attack. If, for example, detectives have begun to interview witnesses, the detectives may be able to offer details that point the CSI to a particular room in a house or to a specific type of evidence. Did an upstairs neighbor hear sounds of a struggle followed by the sound of water running? The CSI would know to check the drains in the bathroom and kitchen sinks.

Focus on the Big Idea

Use the Big Idea question as a way to activate prior knowledge.

PRESENT THE IDEA Read aloud the Big Idea question. Ask students to define *inquiry.* Accept all answers and write them on the board. Help students choose a definition that applies to a crime, possibly "an organized investigation to determine the facts of a case." Then ask students to define *skills* in general (methods used to complete a task).

DISCUSSION QUESTIONS To find out what students know about inquiry skills, ask them what skill would be used to do the following. **Q:** Note that Teacher Y is left-handed. **A:** observing **Q:** State that Candidate X will win an election. **A:** predicting **Q:** Use a stopwatch to time a runner. **A:** measuring

Then tell students that investigators use these and other inquiry skills to solve crimes.

FOLLOW UP See the Teach the Big Idea instruction strategy on TG p. 11.

Forensic Science Videos Video Viewing Guide 1

Discovery Education

VIDEO Clues From a Murder

TIME 6:14 minutes

DESCRIPTION This video focuses on a reenactment of a murder investigation that took place in England in 1784. The video shows how evidence that is collected at a crime scene can be used to convict a criminal. It contrasts techniques available in the 1700s with modern techniques.

TEACHING TIP You could use this video as a preview of the Key Concepts in Chapter 1. The video contains brief references to topics that are addressed in later chapters.

VIDEO The Mysterious Ice Man

TIME 3:01 minutes

DESCRIPTION This video introduces Ötzi, a 5000-year-old mummy that was discovered in the Alps in 1991. The video shows an experiment using shoes similar to those found with the body.

TEACHING TIP Students can find more information about Ötzi online. For example, in 2007 scientists declared a cause of death—blood loss due to an arrow hitting an artery.

VIDEO Interviewing Witnesses

TIME 5:23 minutes

DESCRIPTION This video explains how the amount of evidence an investigator can elicit from a witness depends on the interview technique used by the interviewer.

TEACHING TIP Students may want to practice using the different interview techniques to recall details of an event that all the students observed in the past, such as a school assembly.

Chapter 1 Project SE p. 5

Investigating a Crime Scene

SKILLS OBJECTIVES

After this activity, students will be able to

- make observations and inferences
- secure and sketch a crime scene
- interview witnesses and identify physical evidence

CLASS TIME 60–75 minutes total

Part 1

Make Observations and Inferences

TEACHING TIP Remind students that they use their senses to make observations. Have them test their classification of statements by revising each statement to include a sense. For example, "There were footprints on the floor" can be written as "I saw footprints on the floor." "The thief stood on the couch" cannot be written as "I saw the thief. . ."

Part 2

Secure the Crime Scene

TEACHING TIP Have students make inferences about where the thief went. For example, the thief had to be in the driveway. Also have students consider where investigators are likely to find evidence. For example, if the car hit the stone pillar, the road near the gate should be secured.

Part 3

Sketch the Crime Scene

TEACHING TIP To help students decide which objects to include in their sketches, offer the following guidance. Include objects that were added to the room during the crime, such as the knife. Include objects that were disturbed during the crime, such as the door. Omit objects that don't appear to have been touched during the crime, such as the bust of Sherlock Holmes. (If unrelated objects are large they may be included in the sketch to provide context for the location of other items. For example, if the couch were not a source of evidence, it would still be included in the sketch.)

Part 4

Interview an Eyewitness

TEACHING TIP Tell students that one way to think about which questions to ask an eyewitness is to consider what information would help investigators solve the crime. For example, letters or numbers from a license plate should help investigators to identify the owner of the getaway car.

Part 5

Identify Physical Evidence

TEACHING TIP Encourage students to focus on one object at a time as they make their lists of physical evidence. Remind them that evidence is something that can be used to prove a fact about a crime. So for example, tire tracks could be used to prove the make and model of the tires on the getaway car.

Alternative Crime Scene

To limit the time needed to maintain the crime scene and related locations, have students do all the tasks related to concepts in Chapter 1 after you finish teaching the chapter. Students should prepare search warrants before they collect evidence from suspects. (See SE p. 51 in Chapter 2.)

Review the activities in the Student Edition and the Student Handbook. You might want to choose physical evidence for your crime scene that will allow you to take advantage of the instructions provided. For example, if you want students to use chromatography to analyze ink, you could include a ransom note.

Lesson 1-1 SE pp. 6–13

Using Science to Solve Crimes

Reading Preview

OBJECTIVES

After this lesson, students will be able to

1.1.1 Identify inquiry skills used to solve crimes.
1.1.2 Explain the importance of teamwork in solving crimes.
1.1.3 Compare methods used to solve crimes today with those used in the past.

KEY TERMS

- burglary
- forensic science
- observing
- evidence
- inferring
- predicting
- hypothesis
- crime scene investigator
- medical examiner
- autopsy
- density

Target Reading Skill: Building Vocabulary

Explain that knowing the definitions of Key Terms helps students understand what they read. As students read the lesson, encourage them to make flash cards. Have them write a Key Term on one side of an index card and a definition of the term in their own words on the other side.

SAMPLE ANSWERS

Student answers should contain the most important feature or function of each term. For example, the definition of *predicting* should include a reference to the future.

DIFFERENTIATED INSTRUCTION KEY

Use this key as you review the instructional strategies.

L1 For students with special needs
L2 For less proficient readers
L3 For all students
L4 For gifted and talented students
EL For English language learners

Preteach

Build Background Knowledge: The Five Senses

Ask students to list the five senses and describe how each can be used to make observations. *Sample answer:* smell to detect leaking gas; hearing to detect a gun shot; taste to detect the ingredients in food; touch to measure a person's pulse; sight to notice the license plate on a car.

Discover Activity What Do You Know About Solving Crimes? SE p. 6

SKILLS FOCUS Making Judgments

TIME 10 minutes

TEAM SIZE pair

TIPS Have one student in each pair record the answers to each of the four questions posed in the activity. Encourage students to give reasons for their opinions. Then reconvene as a class to share the results.

EXPECTED OUTCOME All the statements are false. Not all crimes are solved. It can take months or even years to solve a crime. A CSI investigates crimes other than murders. Detectives track and arrest suspects.

THINK IT OVER *Sample answer:* Most people get their information about solving crimes from television shows. Often this source does not give a true picture of how crimes are investigated. For example, on popular shows, the scientists process evidence quickly using highly sophisticated equipment. In reality, many labs have older equipment and a backlog of evidence to be tested.

Instruct

Science at a Crime Scene SE pp. 7–9

Teach Key Concepts: Making Observations

L3 **FOCUS** Tell students that as soon as investigators arrive at a crime scene they begin to make observations. The success of an investigation often depends on the quality of these observations.

TEACH Ask students these questions. **Q:** Has anyone ever borrowed something from your locker or room without asking you? **A:** Most students will say yes. **Q:** How did you know that your space had been disturbed? **A:** Most students will suggest that they observed a change.

APPLY Give each student an unshelled peanut. Ask students not to mark the peanut in any way. Have students record their observations of the peanuts. Collect the peanuts and spread them out on a long table or on several shorter surfaces. Then ask students to find their peanuts. Once the task is done, ask: **Q:** How did you find your peanut? **A:** Students used their recorded observations. **Q:** Which types of observations were most useful? **A:** *Sample answer:* Drawings, measurements, or detailed observations were most useful. Collect the peanuts at the end of the activity.

CAUTION Remind students not to eat the peanuts. If a student in your class is allergic to peanuts or your school has a peanut-free policy, use different objects for this activity, such as acorns and shells.

L1 Ask visually impaired students to use their sense of touch to observe and identify their peanuts.

EL Have students create a list of adjectives that can describe a peanut.

L4 Before students begin, tell them that they will have to prove that the peanut they find is the one they observed.

Teach The Big Idea

Use Visuals: Figure 2

L3 **FOCUS** Read the Big Idea question aloud: What inquiry skills do crime scene teams use as they develop an explanation for a crime? Review the definitions of *observing, inferring, predicting,* and *developing a hypothesis.* Remind students that investigators often make inferences as they develop a hypothesis.

TEACH Tell students that it is possible to make more than one inference from a set of observations. Refer students to Figure 2 (SE p. 8). Ask what they think happened. List their inferences on the board. Then offer three new observations and ask how each observation might affect the list of inferences: (1) An ambulance pulls away from the house. (2) A police officer is talking with the person who lives in the house. (3) The person who lives in the house is performing CPR on a neighbor.

APPLY Find another illustration or photograph from which it is possible to draw more than one inference. Have students use the visual to practice making observations and inferences.

L1 Have visually impaired students work with a partner who can describe Figure 2. Ask the visually impaired students to make inferences based on the description.

Skills Activity — Observing SE p. 7

TIME 15 minutes

TEAM SIZE individual

MATERIALS items such as a pencil stub with tooth marks, a marble, a gum wrapper, a colored paper clip, and a refrigerator magnet

L3 **TIPS** Use different lists so students are not all looking for the same items. Include some small items, some that are not placed at eye level, and some that blend in with the background. Tell students that they can find the items without touching any objects in the room. They should not be opening drawers or looking inside classmates' belongings. Ask students to avoid letting other students know when they have located an item.

EXPECTED OUTCOME Students should realize that some items may be difficult to find because they are small, not at eye level, or blend into the background. Students should realize that careful observation is an important skill in locating evidence.

L1 For a student in a wheelchair, make sure the items on that student's list can be seen from his or her vantage point.

EL Pair a beginning English learner with an English-proficient student who can explain any unfamiliar words on the list.

Address Misconceptions: Observations and Inferences

FOCUS Explain that people sometimes confuse inferences and observations.

TEACH Present this scenario. You have three fish in a bowl in a room. You hear a crash and run into the room. You see broken glass, water, and one fish on the floor. Nearby, your cat is licking its paws. You think, "The cat knocked over the bowl and ate the other fish." Ask students to distinguish observations (broken bowl, missing fish, cat licking its paws) from inferences (cat knocked over bowl and ate fish). Then help students make a general rule they can follow to tell the difference. *Sample rule:* People use their senses to make observations. They use their ability to reason to make inferences.

Help Students Read: Building Vocabulary

L3 Tell students that the word *forensic* comes from the Latin word *forensis*, meaning "public." In Roman cities and towns, trials were held in the public square, or forum.

L2 Help students make a concept map that shows the relationships among the Key Terms in this section of the lesson. Ask students to include definitions on the map.

EL Tell students that the prefix *pre-* means "before." Thus, a prediction is something stated before an event occurs. Offer other examples of words that begin with the prefix *pre-*, such as *prepare, prevent, preview,* and *previous*. Discuss the meanings of these words.

Monitor Progress

L2 **SKILLS CHECK** Tell students that a woman came home from work and found the front door to her apartment open. She saw no obvious signs of damage to the door. Her television was missing. On the floor beneath the empty television stand, she found two candy wrappers. Write the following statements on the board and have students identify the inquiry skill being used for each statement.

a. The front door is open. (observation)
b. The burglar ate some candy. (inference)
c. The burglar stole other items. (prediction)
d. The burglar had a key to the apartment. (hypothesis)

Answers

READING CHECKPOINT (SE p. 7) sight, smell, and hearing

FIGURE 2 *Sample answer:* The person who dropped the groceries may have tripped, been mugged, or run to help someone else. The person may come back to pick up the groceries, or a police officer may come to look at the scene.

FIGURE 3 posing questions

READING CHECKPOINT (SE p. 9) observations and past experiences

Teamwork at a Crime Scene

SE pp. 10–11

Teach Key Concepts: Teamwork

L3 **FOCUS** Ask students if they participate in a sport or other activity (e.g., an orchestra, a debate team, or a chess club) at school that involves teamwork. Ask students how important working together is for the success of the team and have them provide specific examples from their experience.

TEACH Tell students that bringing together a team of people with different skills is essential for a thorough crime scene investigation. Ask a student to name a type of professional who could be found at a crime scene. Write the name on the board and then ask another student to describe that person's role. Continue this process until there are no additional suggestions.

APPLY Tell students that the person who answers a 9-1-1 call is a dispatcher. When a person calls, a dispatcher will ask questions to determine who should be sent to the caller's location. Have pairs of students work together. Ask them to discuss the role of a dispatcher and then write down five questions a dispatcher might ask a caller. *Sample answers:* Where are you? Are you alone? Are you injured?

EL Ask students to describe how emergencies are handled in their countries of origin. Is there a national emergency number? Are there people with roles similar to those described in the text? If students do not know the answers to these questions, have them ask their parents or guardians.

L4 Ask a librarian to recommend and reserve some detective novels for your most proficient readers. Ideally, the novels should have an adult detective or a preteen "detective" who is aided by adults. Ask students to look for examples of teamwork as they read the novels. Have them review the novels both in terms of enjoyment and accuracy of content.

FYI According to the National Emergency Number Association (NENA), about 200 million 9-1-1 calls are made each year in the United States. The vast majority are related to law enforcement.

FYI In most jurisdictions, medical examiners have replaced coroners—public officials who run inquests but are not required to have medical training.

Answers

FIGURE 5 *Sample answer:* A soft brush won't damage the bones and destroy evidence.

READING CHECKPOINT (SE p. 11) The person has to decide who should respond to the call.

Forensic Science Methods SE pp. 12–13

Teach Key Concepts: Technology and Crime Solving

L3 **FOCUS** Hold up a paper clip and a cell phone. Tell students that these items are both examples of technology.

TEACH Explain that technology can be defined as the devices and methods a society designs to meet some human need or desire. Technology allows people to do some things more quickly or with less effort. **Q:** What need does a paper clip serve? **A:** It can be used to gather together individual sheets of paper. **Q:** What desire does a cell phone meet? **A:** It allows people to make and receive phone calls when they are away from their home or place of work.

APPLY Explain that sometimes technology allows people to do things that would not be possible without the technology, for example, exploring outer space. **Q:** What does the technology shown in Figure 7 (SE p. 13) allow a scientist to do? **A:** The scientist can identify the chemical makeup of paint without damaging the painting.

L2 Explain that the term *technology* comes from Greek words meaning "practical" and "science of." People who design technology are applying their knowledge of science to solve practical problems.

Help Students Read: Relating Text and Visuals

L2 Ask students to read the story in Figure 6 (SE p. 12). Then have them read the story again. This time ask them to locate and read the paragraphs in the text that correspond to each panel.

EL Ask students to identify and record any unfamiliar words in Figure 6. Have them use the images to try to figure out what these words mean.

Teacher Demo: Density

TIME 15 minutes

MATERIALS balance, graduated cylinder, water; a gold earring, ring, or pin

PREPARATION Choose an object that will displace a noticeable amount of water when placed in a graduated cylinder. Test to make sure the object will fit in the cylinder and not cause the water to overflow the cylinder.

FOCUS Review the definitions of *mass* (amount of matter) and *volume* (amount of space that matter occupies). Explain that mass or volume alone cannot be used to identify matter because these properties can vary from sample to sample. But mass and volume can be used to calculate density—a property that does not vary from pure sample to pure sample.

TEACH Ask a student to use a balance to find the mass of the object. Record the measurement on the board. Explain that you can use the displacement of water to measure the volume of an object that does not have a regular shape. Fill the graduated cylinder about halfway with water. Demonstrate how to take a volume reading at eye level. Ask a student to read and record the volume. Add the object. Have the student make a second reading. Have students calculate the difference in volume. The difference is the volume of the object. Explain how to find density by dividing the mass in grams by the volume in cubic centimeters.

APPLY Have students compare the density they calculated for the gold object to the density listed for gold in Figure 6. **Q:** Why is the density different? **A:** Some students may know that gold jewelry is not pure gold. Explain that pure gold (24-karat gold) is too soft to be used for jewelry. The gold used for jewelry is a mixture of gold and other metals, such as silver or copper. Fine jewelry is typically 14-karat (58.5% gold) or 18-karat (75% gold). **Q:** How could a person verify that the gold being sold is what the seller claims? **A:** The person could use density to test the claim, just as Archimedes did with the crown.

Background

ANALYZING PAINT The equipment shown in Figure 7 uses an analysis technique called X-ray fluorescence. It depends on the unique electron configurations of elements. When X-rays are absorbed by atoms in the paint, electrons are ejected from inner energy levels in the atoms. This causes the atoms to be less stable. Electrons move from higher energy levels to fill the vacancies. As the electrons move, X-rays are emitted with energies that are characteristic of the elements in the paint.

FYI Long before investigators began using the term *forensic science,* people were devising scientific procedures to help solve crimes. In 1248, the book *Hsi Duan Yu* (The Washing Away of Wrongs) was written in China. The book offers advice on identifying a cause of death. For example, it says to use the presence of water in the lungs to infer drowning.

Answers

READING CHECKPOINT (SE p. 12) density

FIGURE 7 *Sample answer:* Removing paint from the painting would damage the painting.

Assess

Reviewing Key Concepts

1. a. observing, inferring, predicting, developing a hypothesis
   b. Inferences are about what happened in the past; predictions are about what might happen in the future.
2. a. The crime scene investigator records, collects, and tests evidence from a crime scene.
   b. The victim receives medical treatment first because the first responsibility of the crime scene team is to save lives.
   c. Treating an injured person or examining a dead body requires an understanding of human biology.
3. a. a bowl of water and a gold bar; bombard the paint with X-rays and measure the energy given off
   b. A modern investigator has better technology.
   c. *Sample answer:* A crown made of gold and silver has a greater volume than a crown made of pure gold.

Reteach

L2 Refer students to Figure 3 on SE p. 9. Then ask students to provide an example of how each skill is used in everyday life. *Sample answer:* A meteorologist interprets data to predict the weather. A music store arranges CDs into categories. A teacher uses a globe and a flashlight to model the seasons. As movers carry a large object up a narrow stairway, they communicate. People use a scale to measure their weight. While shopping in a supermarket, a person may ask questions such as "Are these pears ripe?" "Do these cookies contain nuts?"

Performance Assessment

L3 **SKILLS CHECK** Give each student a container—a paper bag or a small cardboard box—with an item inside. Use a piece of tape to seal the closed container. (Possible items include a bell, a lemon, a balloon, pennies, keys, and marbles.) Tell students not to open the container. Ask them to use sound, smell, and touch to make observations about the object. Then ask students to make an inference about their object and record reasons for this inference before opening the containers.

L2 **WRITING** Give students a two-column table with five inquiry skills listed in the first column—observing, inferring, predicting, developing hypotheses, and measuring. Have them fill in the second column by describing how Archimedes used each skill to solve the case of the golden crown.

In the Community: 9-1-1

Remind students that pictures rather than words will be easier for young children to understand. Encourage students to think of ways to attract the attention of the children. (They could, for example, use popular cartoon or TV characters.)

Chapter Project

KEEP STUDENTS ON TRACK By now, students should have looked at the illustration of the crime scene on SE p. 1 and recorded their observations and inferences on the worksheet in their Student Handbook.

Skills Lab Who Stole Dave's MP3 Player? SE pp. 14–15

KEY CONCEPT
Investigators use inquiry skills to help solve crimes.

SKILLS OBJECTIVE
After this lab, students will be able to

- distinguish observations from inferences
- develop a hypothesis that is supported by the evidence

CLASS TIME 20 minutes

TEAM SIZE pair

See pp. 15–16 in the Student Handbook, ATE for additional information.

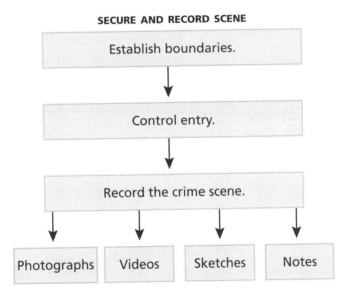

Lesson 1-2 SE pp. 16–21

Securing and Recording a Crime Scene

Reading Preview

OBJECTIVES

After this lesson, students will be able to

1.2.1 Describe how to secure a crime scene.
1.2.2 Identify methods investigators use to record a crime scene.

KEY TERMS

- sketch
- scale
- communicating

Target Reading Skill: Sequencing

Remind students that a sequence is the order in which events occur. Explain that organizing information in a flowchart helps students understand and recall a step-by-step process.

SAMPLE ANSWERS

Students may include the following answers.

SECURE AND RECORD SCENE

Establish boundaries.
↓
Control entry.
↓
Record the crime scene.
↓
Photographs | Videos | Sketches | Notes

DIFFERENTIATED INSTRUCTION KEY

Use this key as you review the instructional strategies.

L1 For students with special needs
L2 For less proficient readers
L3 For all students
L4 For gifted and talented students
EL For English language learners

Preteach

Build Background Knowledge: Controlling Entry

L3 Lead a discussion to elicit experiences students may have had with controlling entry to a space. **Q:** Have you ever tried to keep someone, maybe a little brother or sister, from entering your room or your side of a room? What did you do? **A:** Students may say that they created a boundary of some sort. Tell students that police create boundaries at crime scenes to protect the scene.

L4 Have students think of other instances when the entry to a space is controlled. For example, entry to a subway system can be controlled through the use of turnstiles. At an airport, passengers have to pass through a security checkpoint.

Discover Activity — How Many Footsteps? SE p. 16

SKILLS FOCUS Calculating

TIME 20 minutes

TEAM SIZE individual

TIPS The goal of the activity is for students to get a sense of the magnitude of the intrusion when too many people have unlimited access to a crime scene. The actual average number of steps is not important. Choose a student who sits near the front of the classroom, one who sits in the middle, and one who sits in the back to get an average. Review how to find an average.

EXPECTED OUTCOME Students should realize that investigators need to limit the number of people who are allowed to walk freely through a crime scene.

THINK IT OVER *Sample answer:* The number of total footsteps will depend upon the class size and the size of the room. Police can admit only those persons who have tasks to do at the scene. Police can limit the foot traffic to specific pathways. That way, the crime scene is protected from random foot traffic.

Instruct

Securing a Crime Scene SE p. 17

Teach Key Concepts: How Are Crime Scenes Secured?

L3 **FOCUS** Have students read the introduction on SE p. 16. Then ask the following question. **Q:** Why was Sherlock Holmes angry when he saw the trampled grass at the crime scene? **A:** He realized that the "party with the lodge-keeper" had destroyed tracks left by the killer near the body.

TEACH Explain that investigators must secure a crime scene as soon as possible to protect evidence at the scene. **Q:** How can police secure a crime scene? **A:** They can create boundaries to keep out people other than investigators and establish paths for investigators to use.

APPLY Present a few different crime scenes and ask students how they might secure each scene. Possible examples are a restaurant, a playground, the backyard of a house, and a city sidewalk. Have students discuss what types of natural boundaries they might find at each scene. For example, a backyard may or may not be fenced in.

EL Address any unfamiliar words in the quotation from "The Boscombe Valley Mystery." Even if students have heard the word *wallow*, they are likely to think of "lie down and roll around" rather than "move heavily and clumsily."

L2 Explain that one meaning of *secure* is "to guard or protect." Then show students an image from a book or Web site of a buffalo stampede. Ask students to imagine the ground before and after a herd of buffalo passed through. Then discuss why Sir Arthur Conan Doyle chose this image as an analogy for what could happen if a crime scene were not secured.

Build Inquiry: Keeping a Log

TIME 15 minutes

FOCUS Remind students that the police often keep a log of visitors to a crime scene.

TEACH Have students work in small groups to design the system they would use if they were in charge of keeping the log at a crime scene. Circulate among the groups and, if necessary, ask leading questions such as "What kind of information would you record?" "How would the guards know who to allow in?"

Answers

READING CHECKPOINT (SE p. 17) They tape off a larger area to keep people away from the scene. The larger area provides space to park vehicles, interview witnesses, and meet with other team members.

Recording a Crime Scene SE pp. 18–21

Teach Key Concepts: The Importance of Visual Records

L3 **FOCUS** Ask students what methods people use to record special events such as birthdays, weddings, or vacation trips. Students will probably mention photographs or videos. Some may mention keeping a journal.

TEACH As a class make a list on the board of reasons that a person might make a visual record of an event. (The visuals can help a person remember an event months or years later. The visuals can be shared with someone who could not attend. Visuals often show details that people missed while the event was taking place.) Explain that crime scene investigators have similar reasons for taking photographs. Then ask students to look at Figure 9 and do the Skills Activity on SE p. 19.

APPLY Ask students to find pictures that they think represent each type of photograph in Figure 9. Use magazines, textbooks, or library books. Have students explain their choices.

L1 For visually impaired students, describe each photograph in Figure 9. Ask what a similar set of photographs of their classroom might include.

L4 Have students use the photographs in Figure 9 to write a briet description of a mystery that takes place in Central Park.

Skills Activity Observing SE p. 19

TIME 10 minutes

TEAM SIZE individual

TIPS The photographs were taken in Central Park in New York City. The fountain is called the Angel of the Waters.

EXPECTED OUTCOME In the first photo, you can see the entire fountain. On either side are poles with large banners. In the second photo, less of the fountain is visible, but the viewer can see details of the sculpture. In the third photo, the entire fountain is visible, but the photographer has moved back and to the left. From that position, the viewer cannot see the orange banner but can see fences that were not visible in the first photo. The cup in the close-up isn't visible in the other photos. (The photographer would take a medium-range photo to place the cup in context.)

Use Visuals: Figure 10

L3 **FOCUS** Discuss the floor plan maps found at shopping malls. Explain that these maps display only essential information—the location of the person viewing the map, the names of the stores, and the types of stores. Then state that the sketches a CSI makes at a crime scene also contain only essential information.

TEACH Have students look at Figure 10 (SE p. 20). **Q:** What does the sketch include? **A:** It contains an outline of a room, line drawings of objects, and measurements. **Q:** Why are there no measurements on the scale drawing? **A:** The measurements from the sketch were used to draw the room and the objects to scale. **Q:** How does a person looking at a scale drawing figure out the dimensions of the room and objects? **A:** The person uses the scale provided on the drawing.

L1 Record a description of the sketch and the scale drawing for visually impaired students that they can listen to before class.

Build Inquiry: Making a Sketch

TIME 20 minutes

MATERIALS maps of your community or region

TEACH Ask students to sketch a driving route from one location in the community to another. Pick locations that require a driver to follow a set of instructions. Explain that the map must include landmarks, especially to alert drivers of an approaching turn. Have students use the printed maps to add estimates of the distances between turns on their map.

EXTEND Have students write instructions to accompany their map. Show them an example from a Web site that provides maps.

Skills Activity Calculating SE p. 20

TIME 10 minutes

TEAM SIZE individual

EXPECTED OUTCOME The vault is 3.7 m wide, 4.9 m long, and 3.4 m high.

TIPS Discuss how to convert feet to meters. (Divide the number of feet by 3.28.) Ask students to round their answers to two significant figures to match the data.

FYI Police use a pupil gauge like the one on the notebook in Figure 11 to describe the size of a person's pupils. The size of a pupil can be an indication that the person has been using certain classes of drugs or that the person has sustained a head injury.

Answers

FIGURE 9 *Sample answer:* At a crime scene, there would not be people in the photographs.

READING CHECKPOINT (SE p. 19) long range, medium range, point of view, and close-ups

Assess

Reviewing Key Concepts

1. a. They use crime scene tape, ropes, traffic cones, and parked vehicles.
   b. to limit the opportunities for people to leave objects that will cause confusion when evidence is collected and tested
   c. *Sample answer:* An indoor crime scene would be easier to control; visitors have to enter through doors, which can be guarded.
2. a. photographs, videos, sketches, notes
   b. a close-up; the photographer can use the photo with the ruler to make a print of the object at its actual size.
   c. The CSI should look at a crime scene sketch on which measurements were recorded or at a scale drawing made from the sketch.

Reteach

L3 Make a list of ways that investigators record a crime scene. Discuss the benefits and possible drawbacks of each method. For example, photographs provide more details than a video.

Performance Assessment

WRITING Ask students to choose a task—taking photographs, making sketches, or taking notes. Have students write three instructions to help a person do the task. For taking notes, the instructions could be (1) Carry a waterproof notebook or small voice recorder, (2) Make sure the notes are well organized, and (3) Record what you observed and what you did at the crime scene.

At-Home Activity: Measuring a Room

Refer students to Figure 10 as a guide for drawing doors and windows. If you want students to make measurements in metric units, you may need to loan the students measuring tapes. (Even if you don't require metric measurements, don't assume that every family will have a tape measure.)

Chapter Project

KEEP STUDENTS ON TRACK By now, students should have decided how to secure the crime scene. They should also have made a sketch of the crime scene in their Student Handbook.

Forensics & Earth Science

Mapping Crime SE pp. 22–23

Background The National Institute of Justice is an agency of the U.S. Department of Justice that is devoted to the research, development, and evaluation of programs and technologies to meet the challenges of controlling crime. In 1997, the agency established a Mapping & Analysis for Public Safety (MAPS) program. The program supports the development of mapping software, holds crime mapping conferences, and publishes numerous documents about crime mapping.

Police may use crime maps to solve specific crimes, to allocate resources, and to provide a means of self-evaluation and community review. Some communities publish crime maps on a Web site for public access. Some even allow the public to use the data to make their own maps.

Teacher Demo

LATITUDE AND LONGITUDE

TIME 10 minutes

MATERIALS globe or world map with latitude and longitude lines

FOCUS Tell students that placing a point on a map requires knowing coordinates for that point. Latitude and longitude can be used as coordinates.

TEACH Supply latitude and longitude data for your school and help students find that location on a globe or on a map. Ask students to locate and list cities that are at the same latitude. Have them repeat the task for cities at the same longitude.

Build Inquiry

HOT SPOT ANALOGY

TIME 20 minutes

MATERIALS floor plan of school

TEACH Tell students that breaking school rules is analogous to breaking laws in society. Ask students to predict where the "hot spots" at school are for certain rule violations. Have students work in small groups to make a list of school rules, to devise a visual icon for each rule, and to indicate on a map of the school where violations of these rules are likely to happen.

Go Online

FOR Links on longitude
VISIT www.SciLinks.org
WEB CODE dan-1010

Download a worksheet for students.

In the Community

CRIME MAPPING

Have students research the crime mapping capabilities of local police departments. Ask them to find out if the departments have software for mapping crimes and, if so, what types of maps they make. If local jurisdictions are small, students might need to contact a department in a nearby city. Have students try to get printed copies of maps or identify Web sites where maps can be viewed.

You Be the Judge

1. The mall and the bus station are likely choices. Some students may pick the highway.
2. Discuss how to choose a boundary for a hot spot before students make their graphs. *Sample answer:* There are auto thefts in all the hot spots, but more vandalism at the bus station and near the highway than at the mall.
3. Students may suggest assigning more police or changing the types of patrols as noted in the text. Some students may suggest better street lighting, a neighborhood crime watch, or supervised activities for teens.

Lesson 1-3 SE pp. 24–31

Types of Evidence

Reading Preview

OBJECTIVES

After this lesson, students will be able to

1.3.1 Describe the benefits and drawbacks of direct evidence.
1.3.2 Compare the methods used to help witnesses identify suspects.
1.3.3 Explain why physical evidence is key to solving crimes.

KEY TERMS

- eyewitness
- direct evidence
- modus operandi
- surveillance camera
- physical evidence

Target Reading Skill: Posing Questions

Explain that by changing a heading into a question, students can anticipate the ideas contained within a lesson.

SAMPLE ANSWERS

Students may include the following answers.

QUESTION	ANSWER
What is direct evidence?	The firsthand observations made by an eyewitness are direct evidence.
How are lineups and mug shots used?	Lineups and mug shots are used to help witnesses identify suspects.
How can investigators make a picture of a criminal?	Sketch artists can draw pictures of a suspect based on interviews with eyewitnesses. They can also use images from a surveillance camera and facial recognition software.
What is physical evidence?	Physical evidence is any object that can prove that a fact is true.

DIFFERENTIATED INSTRUCTION KEY

Use this key as you review the instructional strategies.

- **L1** For students with special needs
- **L2** For less proficient readers
- **L3** For all students
- **L4** For gifted and talented students
- **EL** For English language learners

Preteach

Build Background Knowledge: Are Observations Reliable?

Explain that magicians want to control what you observe so that you will not figure out how they do tricks. **Q:** Describe some magic tricks. **A:** *Sample answers:* making objects disappear and reappear; picking a specific card from a pack of cards **Q:** What are some things that magicians do to distract you? **A:** *Sample answer:* They move around the stage, talk, make broad gestures, and direct attention away from certain locations. Tell students that, like a person at a magic show, a witness to a crime can have trouble making accurate observations.

Discover Activity Who Was That Person? SE p. 24

SKILLS FOCUS Observing

TIME 15 minutes

TEAM SIZE individual

MATERIALS an unfamiliar person

TIPS Arrange for a person to make a brief, unexpected visit to your classroom. If possible, choose a person that the students do not know. Otherwise, students will use past knowledge rather than observations to write their descriptions. The person could do something distracting, such as deliver a brightly colored package or sing. You could ask the person to wear something that an observant student might notice, such as a single earring or mismatched shoes.

If you are doing this activity with more than one class, you may need to vary the activity because students in later classes will be prepared for the event. You could use a different person who stays for a shorter period of time.

EXPECTED OUTCOME Most students will realize how difficult it is to make accurate observations when they are not focused on an event or when the time they have to make observations is brief.

THINK IT OVER Most students will find that their first description was not very accurate. Some possible reasons are that they were not paying attention to the visitor or they did not have time to notice many details.

Instruct

Direct Evidence SE pp. 24–25

Teach Key Concepts: Factors That Affect Recall

L3 **FOCUS** Tell students that it can be challenging to recall observations accurately.

TEACH Post ten highly detailed magazine pictures around the room. Cover each picture with another sheet of paper. Assign a group of students to each picture. Once students are gathered in front of a picture, ask them to remove the cover. Give students five minutes to study the images. Then have them replace the cover and return to their seats. Ask students to make a sketch of the picture, with as many details as possible, or write a paragraph describing the picture. Finally, let students compare their sketches and descriptions to the pictures.

APPLY Tell students that with practice they can become better observers. Project a detailed image and tell students that they will have five minutes to make observations. This time, however, do or say things designed to distract the students. When the five minutes are up, turn off the projector and ask students to draw or describe the photograph. Then compare the results from the first trial to the results from the second.

Use the results to discuss factors that affect the accuracy of eyewitness observations. These include a person's physical abilities, experiences, and emotions.

L1 For visually impaired students, use pictures that are not as highly detailed or pictures where the objects are larger and easier to see. Allow students to describe what they observed.

Address Misconceptions: Direct Evidence vs. Hearsay

FOCUS Some people believe everything that they hear, even if it is secondhand or thirdhand.

TEACH Arrange students in several large circles. Give one person in each circle a card with a detailed description of an event. Use a slightly different version for each group. The person with the card should turn to the person on his or her right and tell the story quietly so that others cannot hear it. Have the listener repeat the story to the next person, but without using the card. Continue the process until the person to the left of the original storyteller has heard the story. Ask that person to tell the story to the group. Have the original storyteller read from the card and let the group compare the final description to the original story.

APPLY Ask the following questions. **Q:** What happens when a story gets passed along from one person to another? **A:** Details are left out, added, or changed. **Q:** What do you think the word *hearsay* means? **A:** information that a person is told by another person **Q:** Why do courts not allow hearsay evidence to be used during a trial? **A:** Evidence passed from one person to another is less likely to be accurate.

Monitor Progress

L2 Ask students to determine which of the following people can provide direct evidence. Mr. T. saw a blue van with a white license plate. Mr. P. heard the squeal of tires at 10:05 p.m. Mr. T. told Mr. R. that the robber wore sunglasses. Mr. F. reported seeing a woman with long hair, even though the robber was actually a man. (Everyone but Mr. R. can provide direct evidence.)

Answers

READING CHECKPOINT (SE p. 25) Direct evidence is used in court to prove a fact.

Using Lineups and Mug Shots SE pp. 26–27

Teach Key Concepts: Lineups and Mug Shots

L3 **FOCUS** Explain that police have ways to help witnesses identify a person that they may have seen at a crime scene.

TEACH Explain that police use a lineup when they have identified a suspect and mug shots when they don't have a specific suspect or haven't arrested the suspect. **Q:** What does the witness try to do? **A:** pick out the person the witness saw at a crime scene **Q:** What do the police do to keep the process fair, and why? **A:** They use people who are similar in appearance to make it harder for the witness to pick out a suspect at random.

APPLY Discuss why people might wear a wig, glasses, or other disguises while committing a crime. (These devices make it harder for a witness to give an accurate description of the criminal.)

L1 Use the lineup in Figure 13 (SE p. 26) to help students identify similarities and differences among individuals.

L4 Have students find images of famous people that show the people at different ages. Have students use the images to point out which traits tend to change and which remain constant.

Skills Activity Controlling Variables SE p. 26

TIME 10 minutes

TEAM SIZE pair

TIPS Explain that a variable is a factor or characteristic that can change. Remind students to be sensitive when describing traits related to race, ethnicity, or gender.

EXPECTED OUTCOME Students may list traits such as hair color, skin color, ethnicity, gender, height, weight, facial hair, glasses, and style of clothing.

Build Inquiry: Describing an MO

FOCUS Review the meaning of *modus operandi*—method of operation. Tell students that the term can be used to describe the way a person approaches any task.

TEACH Have students analyze a task such as brushing their teeth. Ask them to write a detailed, step-by-step description of their approach. To help students get started, ask questions such as "What kind of toothbrush do you use?" "Do you start brushing on the left or the right side?"

Monitor Progress

L3 **WRITING** Have students select one suspect from SE pp. 2–3. Ask students to describe three traits they could use to design a fair lineup for the suspect.

Answers

FIGURE 13 *Sample answer:* differences in age, height, and facial hair

READING CHECKPOINT (SE p. 27) photo taken when a person is arrested

Picturing a Criminal SE pp. 28–29

Teach Key Concepts: Sketches Based on Interviews

L3 **FOCUS** Explain that sometimes witnesses can help identify a suspect by working with a forensic artist.

TEACH Discuss the process a forensic artist uses to make a sketch. Compare sketching by hand to sketching using software. Stress that no matter what method the artist uses, he or she must rely on one or more eyewitnesses. The artist needs to ask good questions to get a detailed description from a witness.

APPLY Have students work with a partner. The partners should be seated so that one can view a picture without the other being able to see the picture. Supply a close-up picture of a person's face. Have the student holding the picture describe the person's face. The other student will make a pencil sketch based on the description. The one doing the drawing should ask questions and get feedback from the "witness."

L1 Have students work with a partner who is proficient in English to develop a list of adjectives that can be used to describe facial features. Alternatively, develop the list as a class and write it on the board.

L2 Ask visually impaired students to make a list of adjectives that they could use to describe a person's voice.

Background

TIMOTHY MCVEIGH Investigators found an identification number on the rear axle and a legible license plate on the rear bumper of the rental truck that McVeigh used to transport his bomb. With this information, investigators were quickly able to trace the truck to the rental agency. The owner and two employees helped an artist create a sketch of the man they knew as Robert Kling. After the sketch was made public, the manager of a motel recognized the man who had registered at her motel as Timothy McVeigh. By that time, McVeigh was already in police custody. He had been stopped for driving a car without a license plate and arrested for carrying a concealed gun.

Help Students Read: Compare and Contrast

L2 Have students make a chart that compares the advantages and disadvantages of using sketches, surveillance cameras, and facial recognition software to help identify a suspect. The chart should have three columns. Label the first column Method, the second column Advantages, and the third column Disadvantages.

EL Make a recording of the section on surveillance cameras that students can listen to as they read the paragraphs.

Answers

FIGURE 15 The match is surprisingly good. Students may say that the shape of the eyes, the nose, and the ear lobes could be improved.

READING CHECKPOINT (SE p. 28) a kit containing a library of facial features

Physical Evidence SE pp. 30–31

Teach Key Concepts: Transfer of Evidence

FOCUS Ask students if they have a dog or cat. Then ask if they ever find dog or cat hair on their clothes, on a rug, or on furniture. Discuss how the hairs ended up in those locations.

TEACH Then ask students what they think Locard meant when he said "Every contact leaves a trace." Use the story of the counterfeit coins as an example. Stress that the evidence left behind or taken away may be small and that the person making the contact may be unaware of the transfer.

APPLY Present situations such as the following and ask students to say what physical evidence might be transferred. (1) A person cuts himself while climbing over a barbed wire fence. (blood) (2) A person hides in a barn. (hay, manure) (3) One person scratches another person during a physical struggle. (skin)

Then ask students what they might infer if they observed (1) a paint smudge on the back of a shirt, (2) burrs on pant legs, and (3) a grease stain on a shirt. *Sample answer:* (1) a person leaned against a newly painted wall; (2) a person crossed through a field; (3) a person works in a garage

Use Visuals: Figure 18

L3 Tell students that a microscope with a camera attached to it was used to make the images in the circles. **Q:** What is in the top circle? **A:** hair **Q:** What does 10× mean? **A:** The hairs are 10 times larger than the same hairs seen with the unaided eye. **Q:** What is in the lower circle? **A:** skin **Q:** How does magnifying the skin 650 times affect what the viewer sees? **A:** Details that are not visible with the unaided eye are visible when the skin is magnified. Explain that hairs and flakes of skin are examples of physical evidence.

L1 Have visually impaired students use a hand lens to look at the images.

L2 Explain that the prefix *magni-* comes from the Latin word *magnus* meaning "great" or "big."

Answers

FIGURE 18 Possible answers are soil, small pebbles, or grass.

FIGURE 19 Students are likely to answer that it is easier for modern scientists to solve crimes because of technology. Some students might argue that factors such as population size and the ability of people to move from one place to another make the task harder today.

Assess

Reviewing Key Concepts

1. **a.** firsthand observations of eyewitnesses
   b. Direct evidence is useful when witnesses give accurate descriptions of what they saw and heard. Direct evidence is not always reliable because some descriptions are not accurate.
   c. *Sample answer:* Yes, the detective has experience making and recording observations.
2. **a.** They arrange a lineup or have the witness look at mug shots.
   b. The witness may feel pressured to identify someone.
   c. The witness can look at photos of criminals with an MO that fits the crime or help a forensic artist draw a sketch of the suspect.
3. **a.** *Sample answer:* Physical evidence is any object that can be used to show that a fact is true. Examples are a knife, a hair, and blood.
   b. Physical evidence is transferred.
   c. *Sample answer:* Locard expected metal to be transferred when the suspects made the fake coins. He searched for metal bits in seams and other creases of their clothing.

Reteach

L2 Revisit each figure in the lesson. Ask students to explain the concept being illustrated in each figure. Figure 12, for example, illustrates the concept that eyewitness evidence may not be accurate.

Performance Assessment

L2 **ORAL PRESENTATION** Ask students to contrast a scientist making observations in a lab with a witness making observations at a crime scene. Ask why it is easier for scientists to make accurate observations than for witnesses.

L3 **WRITING** Have students summarize the tools available to the police that can help witnesses identify a suspect.

Writing in Science

WRITING MODE: Descriptive Paragraph

SCORING RUBRIC

4	Exceeds criteria: Uses adjectives to create a vivid, detailed word picture
3	Meets criteria: Includes at least five details that the artist could use to make a distinctive portrait
2	The description has fewer than five details.
1	The artist could not use the description to make a portrait.

Chapter Project

KEEP STUDENTS ON TRACK By now, students should have made a list of questions for the eyewitness and identified useful physical evidence.

Collecting Physical Evidence

Reading Preview

OBJECTIVES

After this lesson, students will be able to

1.4.1 Identify factors investigators consider before searching a crime scene.

1.4.2 Describe methods investigators use to ensure that the evidence found at a crime scene can be used in court.

1.4.3 Explain how investigators protect themselves at a crime scene.

KEY TERMS

• contamination • chain of custody

Target Reading Skill: Outlining

Explain that an outline shows the relationship between main ideas and supporting ideas. An outline helps students organize their information in a logical fashion.

SAMPLE ANSWERS

Students should include the following answers.

COLLECTING PHYSICAL EVIDENCE

I. Organizing a Search
  A. Consider the Crime Scene
  B. Pick a Search Pattern

II. Keeping Evidence Useful
  A. Preventing Contamination
  B. Having the Right Equipment
  C. Packaging Evidence Correctly
  D. Keeping a Chain of Custody

III. Protecting the Investigators

DIFFERENTIATED INSTRUCTION KEY

Use this key as you review the instructional strategies.

L1 For students with special needs	L3 For all students
L2 For less proficient readers	L4 For gifted and talented students
EL For English language learners	

Preteach

Build Background Knowledge: Collecting Evidence

Have students go on a scavenger hunt. A few days before you plan to begin the lesson, give students a list of items to collect and assign a deadline. Depending on your region and the time of year, the list could include items such as a smooth pebble, an acorn, a feather, or a dandelion. Don't supply specific instructions about packaging or labeling. When students bring in their items, note differences in how they package their evidence, including the presence or absence of labels. Explain that packaging and labeling of evidence are important issues for crime scene investigators. (When you discuss organizing a search, you may want to ask students how they organized their searches.)

Discover Activity — How Would You Collect This Evidence? SE p. 32

SKILLS FOCUS Drawing Conclusions

TIME 20 minutes

TEAM SIZE individual

MATERIALS items such as hairs, soil, broken glass, chewed gum, a few drops of fake blood

EXPECTED OUTCOME Students will recognize that different types of evidence require different methods of collection.

TIPS Choose items that would require using different equipment. Place the items at numbered locations around the room so that students can spread out while they are doing the activity.

THINK IT OVER Depending on the evidence, answers might include paper or plastic bags, gloves, tweezers, swabs, or tape.

Instruct

Organizing a Search SE pp. 33–34

Teach Key Concepts: Picking a Search Pattern

L3 **FOCUS** Ask students if they have ever lost something important, such as a house key. Ask students if they found the item, and if so, how they found the item. Did they try to recall where they had been and retrace their steps? Did they look in every possible place in no particular order? Explain that, in general, an organized search is more likely to be successful.

TEACH Tell students that when crime scene investigators search for evidence, they don't always know what they will find. They need to choose a search pattern that that will cover every inch of a crime scene to make sure that evidence is not overlooked. Refer students to Figures 20 and 21. Compare the search patterns and discuss when each pattern would be most useful.

APPLY Return to the example of the house key. **Q:** Which search pattern would be most useful if the key were lost inside a house? **A:** a zone search **Q:** Which pattern would be most useful if the key were lost in a park? **A:** a line search or a grid search

L2 Explain that a grid is a network of evenly spaced horizontal and vertical lines. Graph paper and checkerboards have grids. So do most maps. A zone is a distinct area or region. Use the zones on a basketball floor and time zones as examples.

L1 Ask visually impaired students to describe to their peers how they would search for a lost item. Ask if they would be willing to share with the class methods they have developed for keeping track of their belongings.

Build Inquiry: Search Patterns

TIME 20 minutes

MATERIALS small distinctive object such as an earring, bead, or button

TEACH Hide a small object in the classroom, in a larger room, or outdoors if the weather permits. Give the class a description of the object. If the object is in a room, tell students that the object is not in a drawer or closet. Divide the class into teams and have each team make a plan to find the object. When the plans are complete, have the teams use their plans to search for the object. After a team finds the object, reconvene as a class. Compare the plans and decide which plan was the most efficient, and why.

Math Analyzing Data — Search and Rescue Events SE p. 34

MATH SKILL Reading and interpreting graphs

FOCUS Remind students that a bar graph is used to display data in a number of separate categories. The categories are usually listed on the *x*-axis (the horizontal axis). In this graph, the categories are types of activities.

TEACH Two sets of data are supplied for the categories—the number of events (represented by the blue bars) and the number of injuries or illnesses (represented by the red bars).

NOTE The event statistics are per incident; the injury statistics are per person.

ANSWERS

1. climbing
2. 841
3. about 2.5
4. The ratio of injuries or illnesses to events is higher for climbing than for hiking.
5. *Sample answer:* More people go hiking than climbing in national parks.

Answers

FIGURE 21 zone search; because houses are already subdivided

READING CHECKPOINT (SE p. 33) A CSI might need to do a quick search of an outdoor crime scene because weather conditions could destroy evidence.

Keeping Evidence Useful SE pp. 34–37

Teach Key Concepts: Protecting the Evidence

L3 **FOCUS** Ask students if they or anyone they know has ever had to move from one home to another. Then say that many of the things people have to do when they pack up their belongings are similar to what crime scene investigators have to do when they collect evidence.

TEACH Explain that people who move need to gather the necessary equipment, package items carefully, and keep track of their property. **Q:** What type of equipment might someone who is moving collect? **A:** Possible answers include cartons, tape, tissue paper, newspaper, foam, and felt-tip pens. **Q:** What kinds of items might need extra protection? **A:** Possible answers include items that can break easily, such as mirrors or other glass; furniture that can be scratched; containers of liquids; or plants. **Q:** Why might a person place a label on a carton with a description of the contents? **A:** *Sample answer:* The labels help the person locate an item before all the boxes are unpacked. **Q:** Why would a person keep a record of the number of boxes and the contents when a company is moving the items? **A:** *Sample answer:* The person wants a record to ensure that none of the items disappear en route.

APPLY Have students compare and contrast what a CSI does with evidence at a crime scene to what a person does with items when the person moves. Focus on issues the CSI has that the person who is moving does not have. One example would be the need to package items separately.

L1 Ask the person who receives boxes of supplies or equipment for the school to allow you to open a box in class so students can see how the materials are packaged and labeled.

EL Make black-and-white copies of Figure 22 on SE p. 35. Ask students to translate the labels into their native language. Then have them add annotations in English explaining how each item could be used.

L4 The FBI has developed a comprehensive set of rules for collecting evidence. If students have access to the Internet, suggest they search for the *FBI Handbook of Forensic Services*.

Help Students Read: Use Prior Knowledge

L2 Review the definition of *contamination*—the addition of unwanted material to an object. Offer examples that students might be familiar with, such as oil spills. Remind students that police secure a crime scene to prevent contamination. Then ask what a CSI does to prevent contamination. (A CSI wears protective clothing, such as a head cover, booties, and gloves.)

EL Assemble the equipment listed in Figure 23 (SE p. 36)—cotton swab, forceps, plastic film canister or empty pill bottle, paper bag, and envelope with sealed corners. Display the items and ask students to add labels in English.

Teacher Demo: Chain of Custody

MATERIALS tracking data for a shipped package

TIPS Select a package that made a number of stops between its initial pickup to its final destination. Make a transparency of the data.

TEACH Ask questions such as the following. "When was the package picked up?" "Where was the package on . . . ?" Discuss why companies have a tracking system for packages that are shipped. Explain that the system is similar to a chain of custody for evidence.

Monitor Progress

L3 **ORAL PRESENTATION** Refer students to the photo on SE pp. 4–5. Ask them to describe the clothing worn by the two investigators on the left. Then have them infer why the investigators are wearing gas masks. (Use this discussion as a transition to a discussion of protecting the investigators.)

Answers

FIGURE 22 *Sample answer:* A CSI would place an evidence ruler in a close-up photo of evidence.

READING CHECKPOINT (SE p. 35) tweezers or forceps

FIGURE 23 blood, cigarette butts, hair, or soil

READING CHECKPOINT (SE p. 37) A chain of custody begins when evidence is collected.

Go Online

FOR Links on careers in science
VISIT www.SciLinks.org
WEB CODE dan-1014

Students can download a worksheet that will guide their review of Internet sources on careers in science.

Protecting the Investigators SE p. 38

Teach Key Concepts: Safety

L3 **FOCUS** Explain that crime scene investigators must follow established safety rules to protect themselves at a crime scene.

TEACH Discuss the guidelines for crime scene investigators listed in the textbook. Relate each guideline to the safety rules that students must follow while doing lab activities.

APPLY Divide students into groups of four. Have each team prepare a brief skit about safety at a crime scene. Ask teams to include one error in the skit. Have the other teams try to identify the mistake.

L2 Have students make a poster to illustrate some of the safety guidelines for crime scene investigators.

Assess

Reviewing Key Concepts

1. a. If the search is not organized, the team is likely to miss important pieces of evidence.
   b. the size of the crime scene and the size of the evidence
   c. A line search crosses the area in one direction; a grid search crosses the area twice. (The second search is at a right angle to the first.)

2. a. prevent contamination, have the right equipment, package evidence correctly, and keep a chain of custody
   b. *Sample answer:* The evidence is a small object.

3. a. Possible answers are infected blood, explosives, poisons, or drugs.
   b. They follow established safety rules and procedures.
   c. *Sample answer:* When clothing is torn, dangerous substances can come in contact with a CSI's skin.

Reteach

L2 Remind students that an accurate chain of custody helps show that an item being presented in court is the same item that was found at the crime scene. Refer students to Figure 24 on SE p. 37. Ask students to describe each step in the process. Then ask students to define *contamination.* Finally, ask them how a chain of custody can help prevent contamination of evidence.

Performance Assessment

L3 **SKILLS CHECK** Divide the class into small teams. Set up a number of lab stations equal to the number of teams. Include a different small item of evidence at each station. Provide a variety of tools, packaging, and safety gear at a central location. Ask each team to decide what tool to use to collect the evidence, what packaging to use, and what safety gear the person who collects the evidence should wear.

EL **WRITING** Assign intermediate English learners the task of labeling the evidence to establish a chain of custody.

Math Practice

MATH SKILL: Area

4. The area of the field is 3,200 square meters.

Chapter 1

Chapter Review

Study Guide SE p. 39

Apply the Big Idea

Connect to Key Concepts

Reinforce the Big Idea by connecting it to important Key Concepts. For example, ask "What inquiry skill do investigators need to use when working with other team members?" (communicating) "What inquiry skills might detectives use when interviewing witnesses?" (posing questions, observing) "What inquiry skills does a CSI use while making a sketch of a crime scene?" (observing, measuring)

Connecting Key Terms

Reinforce the Big Idea by connecting pairs of Key Terms. Ask students to write sentences that include two or more Key Terms. Permit students to change the word form of a term. *Sample answers:* A crime scene investigator knows how to collect physical evidence. A forensic artist and an eyewitness must communicate with each other while making a sketch of a suspect.

Review and Assessment SE pp. 40–41

Organizing Information

a. physical evidence **b.** eyewitnesses
c. a lineup **d.** contamination

Reviewing Key Terms

1. b **2.** c **3.** d **4.** a **5.** b
6. False; predicting **7.** True **8.** True
9. False; direct evidence
10. False; contamination

Writing in Science

WRITING MODE: Analogy

SCORING RUBRIC

4	Exceeds criteria: Is accurate, well organized, and focused
3	Meets criteria: Uses examples to compare the packaging of medicines to the packaging of evidence
2	Shows an understanding of ways to prevent contamination, but fails to make a clear comparison
1	Shows little understanding of ways to prevent contamination

Checking Concepts

11. They should try to save lives. Then they should secure the crime scene.

12. They need to show what the crime scene looked like before the evidence was removed.

13. Direct evidence is the observations of eyewitnesses. Physical evidence is an object that can be used to prove that a fact is true.

14. The police can use a lineup when they have a likely suspect. They can use mug shots if the suspect has a criminal record.

15. *Sample answer:* As people move around, they leave some evidence behind. They also carry evidence away from the places they visit.

16. Investigators wear protective clothing to prevent the contamination of physical evidence and to protect themselves from dangerous substances.

Thinking Critically

17. *Sample answer:* Physical evidence may be damaged or lost. Evidence may be added that will confuse the investigation.
18. *Sample answer:* Both the sketch and the scale drawing provide data on the location of objects and the distances between objects. The sketch is rough and not drawn to scale.
19. *Sample answer:* They are likely to use a zone search and make each store in the mall a zone.

Math Practice

20. The area is 312 square yards.
21. Zone A is 9 yards by 6 yards. The area is 54 square yards. Zone D is 13 yards by 1.5 yards. The area is 19.5 square yards.

Applying Skills

22. *Sample answer:* A car crashed into a house. The driver is not at the scene. The person looking at the damage is wearing a hard hat.
23. *Sample answer:* The driver lost control of the car. The driver was injured and was taken to the hospital. The person looking at the damage is concerned that debris may fall off the house.
24. *Sample answer:* Where were you standing when the car hit the house? About how fast was the car going? How many people were in the car?
25. *Sample answer:* Investigators might look for trees or light poles near the street to wrap tape or string around.
26. *Sample answer:* Given the likely size of the property, they could do a zone search of the car and yard.

Chapter Project

PERFORMANCE ASSESSMENT Students should have completed all parts of the project. The presentations should show an understanding of the steps involved in investigating a crime scene. Teams should also address any problems they encountered working as a team.

Chapter 2

Prints and Trace Evidence

Chapter at a Glance SE pp. 42–71

		Resources
Project	**Analyzing Print and Trace Evidence**	• Chapter Project Worksheet
Lesson 1	**Prints** 2.1.1 Describe the kinds of prints investigators look for at a crime scene. 2.1.2 Summarize methods used to preserve and compare prints. 2.1.3 Explain why investigators need search warrants.	• Vocabulary Worksheet • Reading and Note Taking Guide 2-1 • Skills Lab Worksheet • Laboratory Investigation 4: Casting Suspicion • Video Viewing Guide 2 • Video: Tire Tracks Trap Killer
Lesson 2	**Trace Evidence** 2.2.1 Describe how a CSI collects trace evidence. 2.2.2 List five major types of trace evidence. 2.2.3 Explain how crime labs use technology to test trace evidence.	• Reading and Note Taking Guide 2-2 • Laboratory Investigation 5: Splitting Hairs • Laboratory Investigation 6: Lipstick Tells the Tale • Laboratory Investigation 7: A Clear-Cut Case • SciLinks: soil types
	Forensics & Physical Science **Arson Investigations**	• SciLinks: fire triangle • Video: Arson-Sniffing Dogs
Lesson 3	**Identifying Firearms** 2.3.1 Compare the types of evidence that investigators collect when a weapon is fired. 2.3.2 Summarize the methods used to analyze evidence from firearms.	• Reading and Note Taking Guide 2-3 • Video: Firearms Evidence
Review and Assessment		• Chapter 2 Test

Chapter Activities Planner

Activity/Time	Inquiry	Team Size/Materials	Skills
Chapter Project 3 periods	Guided	Team Size: small group newspaper, felt pad, plastic tray, ink in spray bottle, tire tread section, large white paper, filter paper, scissors, graduated cylinder, metric ruler, small plastic cup, stopwatch or clock, pen with water-soluble ink	observing, inferring, drawing conclusions
Lesson 1			
Discover Activity 10 minutes	Directed	Team Size: individual	forming operational definitions
Skills Activity 15 minutes	Guided	Team Size: pair pry bar, chisel, large flat-blade screwdriver, strips of soft wood	drawing conclusions
Skills Lab 45–60 minutes	Directed	Team Size: individual washable black ink, felt pad, plastic tray, large sheet of plain white paper, newspaper, metric ruler, transparency grid, dry erase marker, database of shoe prints	observing, measuring, calculating, classifying
Lesson 2			
Discover Activity 10 minutes	Guided	Team Size: pair coarse sand, hand lens	developing hypotheses
Skills Activity 20 minutes	Guided	Team Size: individual food coloring, white glue, cotton swabs, foam cups	making models
At-Home Activity 45 minutes	Open-ended	Team Size: small group vacuum cleaner, unused filter bag, white paper, plastic gloves, hand lens	observing, classifying
Lesson 3			
Discover Activity 20 minutes	Directed	Team Size: small group plastic spoon, funnel, cornstarch, small balloon, pin	making models
Skills Activity 15 minutes	Guided	Team Size: pair wide plastic straw, scissors, pin, clay, cotton swab	making models

Chapter 2 Prints and Trace Evidence

From the Author

This chapter expands the discussion of physical evidence that began in Chapter 1. It also highlights the connection between what happens at a crime scene and what happens at a crime lab. Some new team members with specific areas of expertise are introduced—a print examiner, an arson investigator, and a firearms expert.

In Lesson 1, students discover that the marks some objects leave on the surfaces of other objects can be important pieces of physical evidence. Lesson 2 focuses on the small bits of physical evidence that could be overlooked if investigators don't do a thorough search. Lesson 3 shows how a firearms expert must be concerned with both marks (on bullets and cartridges) and trace evidence (gunshot residue on a suspect or a victim).

Prints and trace evidence can be combined with other pieces of evidence to build an effective case. But on their own, they cannot be used to positively identify a suspect. Fingerprints and trace evidence containing DNA are the exception. These topics are addressed in Chapter 3.

Background

MAKING CASTS OF IMPRESSIONS The FBI recommends using dental stone to make a cast in soil, sand, or snow. (Other molding plasters are not hard enough to resist abrasion when the cast is cleaned.) Premeasured amounts of dental stone powder can be stored in resealable plastic bags. The CSI can add water to the bag, reseal the bag, and then squeeze the bag vigorously until the mixture is homogeneous.

Pouring a thick liquid directly into an impression could destroy some of the details. So the liquid is usually poured onto the ground next to the impression and allowed to flow slowly into the impression. Some surfaces present challenges. A CSI may spray an impression in soft sand with a lacquer to keep it from falling apart. Impressions in snow are sprayed with wax, and the dental stone is mixed with very cold water to keep the snow from melting.

SEARCH WARRANTS A search warrant is an order signed by a judge or magistrate. Investigators must have "probable cause" to get a warrant. In a sense they need to have some evidence before they can search for additional evidence. Police officers often give the judge written affidavits stating observations made by themselves, witnesses, or informants.

Most searches happen without a warrant. (1) An owner can freely agree to a search of her home. (2) Police officers can seize evidence that is "in plain view." (3) They don't need a warrant to search a person during an arrest. (4) In an emergency, officers can look for weapons that pose a danger to public safety or evidence that can be destroyed.

Evidence that results from an illegal search cannot be used to find other evidence. This concept is referred to as the "fruit of the poisonous tree" doctrine. The "tree" is the evidence found in the initial illegal search. The "fruit" is any evidence found based on the initial evidence.

Focus on the Big Idea

Use the Big Idea question as a way to activate prior knowledge.

PRESENT THE IDEA Read aloud the Big Idea question. Ask students what they know about testing materials.

DISCUSSION QUESTIONS To find out what students know about identifying or comparing materials, ask questions such as the following. **Q:** How can you test for hydrogen or oxygen gas? **A:** You can use a burning wood splint or a glowing wood splint. **Q:** What test could you do to show that a liquid is water? **A:** Measure its boiling point. Pure water boils at 100°C. **Q:** What features could you use to distinguish one type of bird from another? **A:** Answers might include color, size, shape of beak, and song.

Explain that the tests that scientists use to identify and compare materials are similar to the lab tests students do. One main difference is the precision and complexity of the scientists' equipment.

FOLLOW UP See the Teach the Big Idea instruction strategy on TG p. 55.

Forensic Science Videos Video Viewing Guide 2

Discovery Education

VIDEO Tire Tracks Trap Killer

TIME 6:46 minutes

DESCRIPTION This video shows what can happen when police find tire tracks at a crime scene. The tracks are used to identify a brand of tire. Other evidence leads investigators to a car with that brand of tires, and eventually to a friend of the car's owner.

TEACHING TIPS You could use this video both to demonstrate the usefulness of print evidence and to provide an example of effective detective work based on scientific methods.

VIDEO Arson-Sniffing Dogs

TIME 6:43 minutes

DESCRIPTION This video shows a dog working at the scene of a suspected arson. It discusses how dogs detect odors and shows a controlled experiment designed to discover which specific chemicals in gasoline a dog can detect.

TEACHING TIPS You can use this video to reinforce concepts such as observing, teamwork, and the importance of controls in an experiment.

VIDEO Firearms Evidence

TIME 4:24 minutes

DESCRIPTION This video shows how firearms experts gather, test, and analyze evidence from firearms. Actions that would be difficult to illustrate in a textbook, such as test firing a bullet, are clearly shown in the video.

TEACHING TIPS You might want to preview this video. There is an opening scene in which actors simulate a gunfight and murder.

Chapter 2 Project SE p. 43

Analyzing Print and Trace Evidence

SKILLS OBJECTIVES
After this activity, students will be able to
- make tire prints from tire treads
- use paper chromatography to analyze a mixture
- match an unknown object with another object in a database

TEACHING TIP You may decide to do Part 1 of this activity after Lesson 1, and Part 2 after Lesson 2.

Making and Analyzing Tire Prints

PREP TIME 20 minutes

CLASS TIME 45 minutes

TEAM SIZE 5–6 students

MATERIALS 3 different tire tread sections; black ink (washable); 12 tire brand PDF files

SAFETY
Students should wear goggles, a lab apron, and plastic gloves. They should wash their hands thoroughly with soap after the activity.

ADVANCE PREPARATION At www.phschool.com, enter Web Code daf-1000 to access the PDF files. Download the files and print them in color or black and white. Use the prints to assemble a database of tire brand photographs.

Wash the tire tread sections with soap and water and dry them. Washing will remove oil residue from the manufacturing process or ink applied by a previous class.

BEGIN THE PROJECT Tell students that they will be given a tire tread section that matches the tread on a tire that left prints at the crime scene. Students will make a print of the tire tread and compare it with a database of tire brand photographs. After students identify the brand of tire that left the prints at the crime scene, they will be able to narrow their list of suspects. Point out that several suspects will have the same brand of tire. (Refer to SE pages 2–3.)

TEACHING TIPS You might need to set up only 1 or 2 inking stations for the entire class. Keep track of which teams receive which tire tread sections.

Have students place several sheets of newspaper under the clean sheet of white paper. The newspapers will provide a cushion and allow students to obtain a better print. Warn students to be careful not to get ink on skin, clothing, or other items that the ink could stain.

Do not display the database of tire brand photographs until all the students have turned in their tire tread sections. Letters are used instead of brands to label the photos so that students will look at all 12 photos. Use the TireBrandKey.pdf file to match the letters to tire brands. Some teams may select a letter that does not match one of the tire brands owned by the suspects. If so, tell students that they have not made a correct identification and to try again.

DISPOSAL All materials may be disposed of in the trash.

EXPECTED OUTCOME The tire prints should include plenty of details from the tire tread, including any letters and numbers that are molded into the tread. Students should be able to use the tread pattern and any additional identifying marks to match their print to a photograph in the database.

Part 2

Analyzing Ink With Paper Chromatography

PREP TIME 45 minutes to make pen brand chromatograms

CLASS TIME 45–50 minutes

TEAM SIZE 5–6 students

MATERIALS 3 pens with water-soluble black ink, different brands; filter paper, 15-cm, medium flow

SAFETY
Students should wear goggles, a lab apron, and plastic gloves. They should wash their hands thoroughly with soap after the activity.

ADVANCE PREPARATION Follow the directions in Part 2 of the student procedure to make a sample chromatogram for each brand of pen that students will be testing. When the chromatograms are dry, label one "Click," another "Glide," and the third "Penz." Display the chromatograms in the classroom.

Fold a piece of filter paper in half twice. Unfold the paper and use a pen to draw a solid circle of ink with a 1.5-cm diameter in the center of the paper. Allow at least one hour for the ink to dry completely. Make one inked filter paper for each team. Make at least one sample using each brand of pen. If there are six teams, for example, make two samples from each pen. Keep track of which team receives which ink.

Make a few extra inked samples in case students have a problem with Step 12 of the procedure.

BEGIN THE PROJECT Remind students that the thief left a ransom note at the crime scene. Tell students that forensic scientists isolated the ink from the ransom note. The scientists also used paper chromatography to analyze ink from the three brands of pen owned by the suspects. Show students where the ink chromatograms are displayed.

Tell students that they will be testing ink from the ransom note. If they can match their results with one of the posted samples, they will know which brand of pen was used to write the ransom note. Point out that several suspects have the same brand of pen. (Refer to SE pages 2–3.)

TEACHING TIPS When you distribute the ink samples, don't tell students that the ink they receive might be different from the ink that other teams receive.

When students do Step 9, suggest that they roll the pie-shaped section of filter paper around a pencil to form a cylinder. After students remove the pencil, they should adjust the rolled paper until it is cone shaped. Students should not use staples or tape.

Make sure that the cut line students make in Step 12 is curved so that students end up with a circular hole. If students cut too big a hole, there will not be enough ink left on the paper to analyze. If this happens, don't simply add more ink to the paper because the ink will not have enough time to dry. Instead, give the team a new piece of inked filter paper. If students have trouble cutting a proper size hole, you may want to make the cuts yourself.

When students place the inked filter paper and filter paper cone assembly on the rim of the cup in Step 13, the cone may slip down so it is no longer touching the inked paper. If that happens, have students pull the cone up so the cone touches the entire hole.

EXPECTED OUTCOME It takes 20–30 minutes to complete the chromatography. All water-soluble inks should spread out evenly over the filter paper. Inks that are a mixture of colors should separate into those colors. The sample data in the Student Handbook is based on 15-cm, medium flow filter paper. If you use different filter paper, you may need to adjust the time intervals for measuring the distance traveled by the ink.

DISPOSAL All materials may be disposed of in the trash.

Alternative Crime Scene

At this point in the project, students should be testing and comparing trace evidence that they collected from the crime scene or from the suspects. They should narrow their list of suspects based on the results. (Depending on the evidence, students may be able to identify a single probable suspect.)

Lesson 2-1 SE pp. 44–51

Prints

Reading Preview

OBJECTIVES

After this lesson, students will be able to

2.1.1 Describe the kinds of prints investigators look for at a crime scene.
2.1.2 Summarize methods used to preserve and compare prints.
2.1.3 Explain why investigators need search warrants.

KEY TERMS

- print
- imprint
- impression
- skid mark
- cast
- search warrant

Target Reading Skill: Previewing Visuals

Explain that looking at visuals before reading will help students recall prior knowledge and allow them to predict what they are about to read.

SAMPLE ANSWERS

Students may include the following answers.

IMPRESSIONS AND CASTS
Q. What is an impression?
A. An impression is a pattern left when an object is pushed into a surface—either the surface is soft or the object is pressed hard against the surface.
Q. What is a cast?
A. A cast is an object made by filling a mold with a liquid that takes the shape of the mold as it changes to a solid.

DIFFERENTIATED INSTRUCTION KEY

Use this key as you review the instructional strategies.

L1	For students with special needs
L2	For less proficient readers
L3	For all students
L4	For gifted and talented students
EL	For English language learners

Preteach

Build Background Knowledge: Footprints

L3 Discuss the evidence dinosaurs left behind—bones and tracks preserved in stone. Talk about how scientists use these tracks, along with bones, to determine the size of dinosaurs. Explain that detectives can use similar evidence left by humans to solve crimes.

L2 Borrow a book about dinosaurs or search online for a site that has photographs of dinosaur tracks.

Discover Activity What's the Difference? SE p. 44

SKILLS FOCUS Forming Operational Definitions

TIME 10 minutes

TEAM SIZE individual

TIPS Ask students if any of them have prints of their feet that a parent made when they were born.

EXPECTED OUTCOME Both prints were made by a left foot, but not the same left foot. The key difference is that one print is flat and one has depth.

THINK IT OVER *Sample answer:* An impression is a mark that has depth—that is not flat.

Instruct

Types of Prints SE pp. 45–48

Teach Key Concepts: Recognizing Patterns

L3 **FOCUS** Discuss how the desks or tables in a classroom are arranged in an orderly, predictable way. This arrangement is an example of a pattern. The pattern can vary among classrooms. Explain that one meaning of the word *pattern* is a regular or repeated form, order, or arrangement.

TEACH Ask these questions. **Q:** What objects in nature have patterns that can be used to identify the objects? **A:** *Sample answers:* animal skins, shells, flowers, sedimentary rocks, and birds (color patterns). **Q:** What manufactured items have patterns? **A:** *Sample answers:* wrapping paper, paper towels, floor tiles, and sheets. Explain that most of these patterns are distinctive, but not unique. The markings on animals are an exception. They can be used to distinguish one individual from another.

APPLY Explain that investigators look for marks left by objects, such as shoe soles, that have distinctive patterns. Then say that two people who have the same size shoe buy identical pairs of shoes. **Q:** When the shoes are new, could you tell which pair left a shoe print? **A:** No, because the soles have identical patterns. **Q:** After the shoes are worn for a few months, could you tell which pair left a shoe print? **A:** Yes, because the soles will be worn down more in some places than in others, which will produce a distinctive pattern. The soles will also have cuts and scratches.

L1 Discuss how patterns of raised dots are used in Braille code.

L2 Display actual objects or photos of objects when discussing the patterns on natural and manufactured objects.

Background

SHADOW WOLVES The Shadow Wolves patrol a 76-mile border between Mexico and Arizona's Tohono O'odham Nation reservation. The unit, which was established in 1972, is now part of the Department of Homeland Security. The unit calls what it does "cutting for sign," which means searching for and analyzing physical evidence.

FYI The classification of prints into imprints and impressions follows the system used by the Connecticut Forensic Science Laboratory. Not everyone uses the same terminology for prints. Imprints often are called two-dimensional impressions.

Build Inquiry: Tire Treads

TIME 30 minutes

MATERIALS 2 or 3 different tires, white paper (8.5" × 11" or larger)

L3 **TEACH** Have teams of students make rubbings of at least two tires. This activity will work best if one person presses the paper against a tire tread while a second person rubs the side of a pencil across the paper. Have students use Figure 3 on p. 46 of their textbook to add labels to the rubbings. Then have them circle any marks that an investigator might be able to use to distinguish the tire from other similar tires.

L1 A visually impaired student could run a gloved hand across two different tire treads and describe differences in the patterns.

L4 Explain that the grooves in a tire tread channel water from the front to the back of a tire when it rains. Large, deep grooves are more effective at preventing hydroplaning. But large grooves provide less traction on dry roads. So the design of all-weather tires is a compromise. Then ask students why some race drivers use smooth tires with no grooves. (For races that take place only when the track is dry, drivers want as much contact with the road as possible.)

FYI Skid marks are most often used as evidence in vehicle crash reconstructions. With anti-lock brakes that pulse, skid marks will be discontinuous.

Math Analyzing Data — Estimating Speed From Skid Marks SE p. 48

MATH SKILLS interpreting graphs, estimating

FOCUS Remind students that skid marks are left on a road surface when a driver applies the brakes and the wheels lock.

TEACH Remind students to determine which data are on the *x*-axis (speed in mph) and the *y*-axis (length of skid in feet). Then ask students why there are three lines on the graph. (Each line displays data for a different road surface.)

ANSWERS

1. about 71 feet
2. about 45 mph
3. snow; asphalt
4. The higher the speed, the longer the skid.

Skills Activity Drawing Conclusions SE p. 47

TIME 15 minutes

TEAM SIZE pair

MATERIALS pry bar, chisel, large flat-blade screwdriver, strips of soft wood (balsa or pine)

L3 **TIPS** While wearing goggles, use the tools to make marks on the wood strips. (You may need to use a hammer to make the marks.) Label the marks made by the first tool A, the marks made by the second tool B, and so on. If the class is large, make several sets of strips with marks.

EXPECTED OUTCOME Students should be able to identify the tool that made each mark by observing the shape and size of the blades.

L1 Allow visually impaired students who are wearing gloves to feel the tools and the marks. **Caution:** You should supervise this activity. A chisel blade can be quite sharp.

L4 You can increase the challenge by using a pry bar, chisel, and screwdriver with similar-sized blades. Or use two tools of the same type and vary the blade size or the amount of wear.

Teacher Demo: Tools

TIME 10 minutes

MATERIALS a pry bar, chisel, and screwdriver

FOCUS Explain that the shape of the working edge, or blade, of a tool reflects the tasks the tool is designed to do.

TEACH Hold up each tool so that the students can see it, or pass the tool around the class. **Q:** What is this tool called and how is it normally used? **A:** A pry bar can be used to remove nails or paneling from a wall. Some chisels are used to cut and shape wood. A screwdriver is used to insert or remove screws. **Q:** How might a burglar use these tools? **A:** *Sample answer:* The pry bar may be used to pry open a window. The chisel may be used to scrape away wood from around a lock or hinge. A screwdriver may be used to remove a lock.

Monitor Progress

L2 **WRITING** Ask students to explain why investigators look for marks made by shoes, tires, tools, and gloves.

EL **ORAL PRESENTATION** Have students describe what they observe in Figure 2 on SE p. 45. Then ask them how what they observe would affect prints made by those boots.

Answers

READING CHECKPOINT (SE p. 45) shoe size and the pattern on the sole

FIGURE 2 *Sample answer:* There are distinctive wear patterns on the soles, including holes.

FIGURE 4 *Sample answer:* The engine may have taken too sharp a turn at the corner.

FIGURE 5 The chisel would leave a broad mark. The pry bar would leave a pair of narrower marks.

READING CHECKPOINT (SE p. 47) The examiner would look for flaws on the blade of the tool.

Preserving Prints SE pp. 48–49

Teach Key Concepts: Save That Print

L3 **FOCUS** Ask students what people do when they want to have a record of a special object that will not last—a birthday cake, a sand castle, or an ice sculpture. (Students are likely to suggest taking photographs.)

TEACH Remind students that investigators need a record of all physical evidence at a crime scene. Some methods that work for other physical evidence work for prints, for example, taking photographs. Some methods are specific for prints, for example, making a cast of an impression.

APPLY Ask students to look at Figure 6 on SE p. 48. **Q:** Why is the light placed low to the ground? **A:** A light at a low angle creates shadows that highlight details in the impression. **Q:** Why is a ruler shown in at least one shot? **A:** The ruler is used to show the size of the impression.

EL Make sure students understand what *preserve* means. The word has multiple meanings, but in this context the synonym *save* may be most useful. Sometimes an actual print can be saved and taken to the lab. Sometimes, a copy of the print—a photograph or a cast—is saved instead.

Use Visuals: Figure 7

L3 **FOCUS** Explain that making casts is one way to preserve impressions.

TEACH Ask students to look at Figure 7 on SE p. 49. **Q:** Which of the three objects shown can act as a mold, and why? **A:** The impression can act as a mold because it can be filled with a liquid. **Q:** List the steps for making a cast. **A:** Fill the impression with liquid. Let the liquid set. Remove the cast. Explain that the cast is a mirror image of the impression. **Q:** Which other object in Figure 7 is a mirror image of the impression? **A:** the shoe

L1 Have visually impaired students put on gloves and feel the bottom of a shoe. Ask them to describe what they feel. Then ask them to predict how a cast made from the shoe would feel.

Build Inquiry: Making a Cast

TIME 20 minutes the first day, 10 minutes the second day

MATERIALS object with distinctive pattern, foam tray, modeling clay, oil or nonstick cooking spray, measuring cups, paper cup, plaster of Paris, craft stick, rolling pin (optional)

ADVANCE PREPARATION Ask students to bring in a small object that has some raised detail on its surface, such as a shell, dye stamp, or golf ball. Provide items for students who do not have an appropriate item.

TEACH Give each student a foam tray. Meat trays from a grocery store work well. **Caution:** Clean the trays thoroughly. Give each student enough clay to make an impression of the student's object. The clay should be thick enough when pressed or rolled out so that at least ½" of clay is left beneath the object when it is pressed completely into the clay.

Before students press their object into the clay, have them rub oil on the object or spray it with nonstick cooking spray. This step will make it easier to remove the object without damaging the impression.

Have students pour ¼ cup of water into a large paper cup. Then have them slowly pour ½ cup of plaster of Paris into the water while stirring it with a craft stick. The mixture should have the consistency of pancake batter. Have students slowly pour the plaster of Paris into the impression. Let the setup sit for 24 hours. Then have students carefully remove the clay to expose the cast. Remind students that plaster of Paris is fragile and can break easily. Have students compare the cast to the object.

Monitor Progress

L3 **WRITING** Ask students to describe one advantage of each method for preserving print evidence.

Answers

FIGURE 7 *Sample answer:* It would be easier to compare a shoe to a cast because the cast is not a mirror image of the shoe. But the impression is.

READING CHECKPOINT (SE p. 49) An impression can be filled with a liquid that takes the shape of the impression as it hardens.

Comparing Prints SE p. 50

Teach Key Concepts: Using Databases to Compare Prints

L3 **FOCUS** Explain that most libraries keep a catalogue of their books online. The catalogue contains a record for each book. The way data are stored in the record allows people to use different characteristics to search for a book—author, title, subject, and so on. The catalogue is a database.

TEACH Explain that when investigators find a shoe print at a crime scene, they may be able to use a database to find the brand and model of shoe. **Q:** To begin the search, what is the first thing the print examiner must do? **A:** add a record and a scanned image of the shoe print to a database of crime scene prints **Q:** What can the print examiner do next? **A:** search for similar prints in the database **Q:** What other kinds of data can be found in a shoe print database? **A:** shoe prints from suspects and data supplied by manufacturers about makes and models of shoes

APPLY Explain that when a computer program searches for prints, it doesn't compare the images. It compares data stored in the records and then displays the images of prints with similar characteristics. Ask students to suggest characteristics of a shoe print that might be included in a record. The obvious choices are length and width. A technician also codes for elements in the pattern on the sole—zigzags, diamonds, and so on.

L4 Have interested students work together to devise a coding system for the database of shoe prints from the Skills Lab.

Answers

READING CHECKPOINT (SE p. 50) prints from crime scenes, prints from companies that manufacture shoes, and prints from suspects

FIGURE 8 The examiner is measuring the width of two ribs.

Search Warrants SE p. 51

Teach Key Concepts: What Makes a Search Legal?

L3 **FOCUS** Ask students to recall television shows or movies in which a police officer knocks on a door and shows the person who responds a search warrant. Ask students what happened next. (Generally, a team of officers enters the location, searches everywhere, and leaves with items.)

TEACH Explain that there are two main reasons that police need a search warrant. The U.S. Constitution requires that a suspect's rights be protected. If a search is not legal, the evidence collected may not be able to be used in court. Discuss what police must do to obtain a search warrant and the type of information the warrant must contain.

APPLY Refer students to the burglary described in Chapter 1, Lesson 1. Tell students that the police have identified a suspect for the burglary. **Q:** What items should investigators list on the search warrant for the suspect's home? **A:** stamp collection, shoes, tools, perfume

L1 Use an analogy. Ask what has to happen before a student can go on a field trip? (The student will need a signed permission slip from a parent or guardian.)

Help Students Read: Build Vocabulary

EL If the terms *reasonable* and *unreasonable* are unfamiliar, give examples of behaviors. Ask students to pick the correct term to describe each behavior. For example, is it reasonable to go outside in a snowstorm wearing only shorts and a T-shirt?

Assess

Reviewing Key Concepts

1. **a.** Prints made by these objects have a distinctive pattern.
   b. *Sample answer:* The tool may have been stolen or borrowed.
   c. the print from the older shoe because the wear pattern will help distinguish the shoe from all other similar shoes that were sold
2. **a.** removing the object and sending it to the lab for analysis
   b. Casts and photographs are ways to record impressions. Casts, which are three-dimensional, can show more details than photographs.
   c. *Sample answer:* Databases provide a large number of possible matches and reduce the amount of time needed to do a search.
3. **a.** A warrant protects a suspect's rights; it ensures that a search is legal.
   b. The search is not reasonable because the police cannot explain why they expect to find the tool in every house.

Reteach

L2 Help students make a flowchart showing the sequence of events from the discovery of a tire tread impression at a crime scene to the comparison of a cast to a tire print at the crime lab.

Performance Assessment

L2 **SKILLS CHECK** List the following words on the board—*impression, mold, cast, imprint.* Ask students to use one of the words to describe each of the following objects—an ice cube tray (mold), ice cubes (cast), tire track in mud (impression), and a skid mark (imprint).

L3 **WRITING** Have students write a story that would help fourth grade students understand what a search warrant is and why it is important.

Writing in Science

WRITING MODE: Descriptive Paragraph

SCORING RUBRIC

4	Exceeds criteria: Uses adjectives to create a detailed word picture of the shoes
3	Meets criteria: Includes specific details that make it possible to identify the shoes
2	The details are not specific enough to identify the shoes.
1	The description is general with little detail.

Chapter Project

KEEP STUDENTS ON TRACK By now, students should have made a print of a tire tread and compared the print to photos in a tire brand database.

Skills Lab Analyzing Shoe Prints SE pp. 52–53

KEY CONCEPT
Forensic scientists use computer databases to identify and compare prints. They also compare prints found at a crime scene to objects that belong to a suspect.

SKILLS OBJECTIVES
After this lab, students will be able to

- make a print of a shoe sole
- observe and record characteristics of a shoe print
- compare a print to a database of similar shoe prints

CLASS TIME 45–60 minutes

TEAM SIZE individual

See pp. 49–52 in the Student Handbook, ATE for additional information.

Trace Evidence

Reading Preview

OBJECTIVES

After this lesson, students will be able to

2.2.1 Describe how a CSI collects trace evidence.
2.2.2 List five major types of trace evidence.
2.2.3 Explain how crime labs use technology to test trace evidence.

KEY TERMS

- trace evidence
- classifying
- concentration
- chromatography
- microscope

Target Reading Skill: Using Prior Knowledge

Explain that prior knowledge is what you already know before you begin to study a topic. Building on what is already known can help students learn new information.

SAMPLE ANSWERS

Students may include the following answers.

WHAT YOU KNOW
1. Hair varies in color and length. 2. There are many colors of paint. 3. Glass breaks easily. 4. Soil contains small pebbles and dirt.

WHAT YOU LEARNED
1. Hair is made up of layers. 2. There is a database for paint samples called the PDQ. 3. Scientists can use the concentration of elements in glass to compare glass samples. 4. Scientists can analyze the composition of soil and match a soil sample to a specific location.

DIFFERENTIATED INSTRUCTION KEY

Use this key as you review the instructional strategies.

- **L1** For students with special needs
- **L2** For less proficient readers
- **L3** For all students
- **L4** For gifted and talented students
- **EL** For English language learners

Preteach

Build Background Knowledge: Traces of Evidence

Suggest to students that someone made a cake and left a note that says "Do Not Touch!" You take a bit of frosting, thinking no one will notice. But the person who made the cake accuses you of touching the cake. **Q:** How did the person know? **A:** Perhaps there is frosting on your face (or you left a mark when your finger scraped the cake). Explain that even a tiny bit of physical evidence can be found and used in a criminal investigation. This type of evidence is called trace evidence.

Discover Activity — What Clues Does Sand Contain? SE p. 54

SKILLS FOCUS Developing Hypotheses

TIME 10 minutes

TEAM SIZE pair

MATERIALS coarse sand, hand lens

TIPS Even without a hand lens, students should be able to notice particles of different colors in coarse sand. Have students spread the sand on white paper.

EXPECTED OUTCOME

1. There is likely to be one predominant color and two or three other colors.
2. With coarse sand, the particles would be more like poppy seeds.
3. Possible answers are shape of particles and luster.

THINK IT OVER Any answer that focuses on the properties of the sand is reasonable.

Instruct

Collecting Trace Evidence SE p. 55

Teach Key Concepts: Knowing Where to Find Evidence

L3 **FOCUS** Remind students that trace evidence, like all physical evidence, can be left at a crime scene or taken away from a crime scene.

TEACH Have students work in pairs. Ask students to read the section titled "Knowing Where to Look." As they read, have them make a list of trace evidence that was left at the crime scene and a list of trace evidence that was taken from the crime scene. Then have a class discussion about what method an investigator could use to collect each piece of evidence.

EL Pair English-language learners with students who are proficient readers.

L4 Explain that investigators don't collect every object that they observe at a crime scene. They look for items that seem out of place. Say that a man struggles with a burglar. A CSI finds cat hairs on the man's jacket. **Q:** Should the CSI collect the hair? **A:** yes, if the man does not have a cat

Answers

FIGURE 10 tape

READING CHECKPOINT (SE p. 55) The CSI needs a search warrant.

Types of Trace Evidence SE pp. 56–59

Teach Key Concepts: Classifying Trace Evidence

L3 **FOCUS** Explain that trace evidence can be organized into five major categories: hair, fibers, paint, glass, and soil.

TEACH Present the following scenario. A person breaks a ground floor window at a school, crawls through, spray paints a message on the wall in the lobby, and leaves. Ask students to predict which types of trace evidence the person might have left at the crime scene (soil, fibers, hairs) and which types the person may have taken away (soil, paint, glass).

APPLY Divide the class into small groups. Assign each group one type of trace evidence. Ask the groups to decide which four things a forensic scientist needs to know about their assigned type of evidence. Remind students to use both the text and the illustrations.

L2 Use soil as an example to show students how to do the Apply activity.

L4 Ask students to predict which of the pieces of trace evidence identified for the initial scenario would be most useful for connecting a suspect to the crime. Ask them to provide reasons for their predictions.

Build Inquiry: The Structure of Hair

TIME 25 minutes

MATERIALS light microscope, prepared slides of hair samples

L3 **FOCUS** Use Figure 11 on SE p. 56 to introduce the structure of hair and the possible differences between hair samples.

TEACH Use Appendix B on p. 152 of the SE to discuss the use of a microscope. Ask students to view the prepared slides under low power and high power. Have them draw what they observe in their notebooks.

APPLY Ask students to compare two hair samples that are noticeably different and make a list of the differences. As a class, discuss how an examiner might use these differences.

L4 Have students make slides of their own hair. Provide slides, cover slips, a dropper, and water. Review the instructions in Appendix B on p. 153 of the SE for making slides.

Use Visuals: Figure 12

L3 **FOCUS** Tell students that one meaning of the word *structure* is "how the parts of an object are put together." Explain that different types of fibers have different structures.

TEACH Explain that the images shown in the circles were made using a microscope and a camera. **Q:** What are the objects in the circles? **A:** fibers that are used to make clothing **A:** Which of the fibers are natural fibers? **A:** wool and cotton **Q:** What do wool fibers have in common with human hairs? **A:** They have scales on their surfaces.

APPLY Tell students that detectives have found a fiber at a suspect's home that matches fibers found at a crime scene. **Q:** Is this match positive proof that the suspect was at the crime scene? **A:** no, because objects made from the same type of fiber may be found in many homes

L1 Describe the photographs in Figure 12 to visually impaired students.

L2 Tell students that the adjectives *natural* and *synthetic* are opposites. Have students find information in the text to support the labeling of cotton and wool fibers as natural, and the labeling of polyester as synthetic.

Teach the Big Idea

Use Visuals: Figure 13

L3 **FOCUS** Read aloud the Big Idea: How do investigators identify and compare materials they find at a crime scene?

TEACH Ask students to look at Figure 13 on SE pp. 58–59. Explain that the car was involved in a hit-and-run. **Q:** What trace evidence was found at the crime scene? **A:** paint chips and glass from a headlight **Q:** How was the paint used to help locate the car? **A:** A forensic scientist analyzed the paint. Then a technician used the PDQ database to identify possible makes and models of cars with that type of paint.

Tell students that the investigators also had direct evidence. A witness was able to recall a few numbers from the license plate and identify the state. **Q:** How could investigators use this evidence to help find the car? **A:** They could use the partial plate number plus the make and model data to search the database at the registry of motor vehicles.

State that the search revealed a few possible suspects. The police then contacted local body shops and found that one of the cars was in a shop for repairs. They used this information to obtain a search warrant. **Q:** Once investigators have the car, what can they do? **A:** They can collect a paint chip to compare to the chips at the crime scene. They could compare bits of glass collected at the crime scene to the broken headlight. They could compare soil on the wheels with soil from the crime scene.

L1 If you do an online search using the phrase *forensic paint layers,* you should find photographs that you can show to visually impaired students. You can use the phrase *pollen grains* to find SEM images of pollen.

EL Ask students if they have ever used a frozen concentrate to make orange juice. Explain that water is removed from orange juice to form the concentrate. When the water is removed from the juice, the concentration of all the substances in the juice other than water increases. When water is added to the concentrate, the concentration of all these substances decreases.

L4 Borrow a reference book with photographs of flowering plants and pollen, or have students search for such photographs online. Students can use the reference book to make drawings for a poster about different types of pollen. Or they can capture screen grabs of photos to use in an online report.

Background

GLASS Forensic scientists previously were able to use density and refractive index to compare samples of glass. Improvements in the manufacture of glass have made these properties less useful. Now a scientist is more likely to rely on the concentration of trace elements in glass.

FYI On most newer cars, the large glass headlamps have been replaced with small glass lamps behind a plastic lens.

Skills Activity   Making Models SE p. 58

TIME 20 minutes

TEAM SIZE individual

MATERIALS food coloring, white glue, cotton swabs, foam cups

PREPARATION Cut foam cups so students have containers with a depth of about 1". Make three 2"-deep master containers. Squeeze white glue for ten seconds into each master container. Add three drops of blue food coloring to the first master container, six drops of red to the second container, and three drops of yellow to the third.

Use a swab or craft stick to mix the food coloring with the glue. Leave, or place, a swab in each container. The mixtures will stay liquid for about three hours after preparation.

TIPS If you want a more orderly display, use only two colors and assign students a ratio of dabs—1 : 1, 1 : 2, 2 : 1, 2 : 3, and so on.

EXPECTED OUTCOME Student mixtures should dry within 45 minutes. Students should realize that changing the composition of the paint changes the color of the paint.

Monitor Progress

L3 **WRITING** Have students pick one of the five types of trace evidence and write a paragraph about how this type of evidence can be used to help identify a suspect. Students should include a description of the type of evidence and the characteristics a scientist would use to compare samples.

Answers

FIGURE 11 *Sample answer:* The cells in the dog hair are circular; the cells in the cat hair are shaped liked hemispheres.

READING CHECKPOINT (SE p. 57) Natural fibers come from animals and plants. Synthetic fibers are developed by chemists in labs.

FIGURE 13 *Sample answer:* If investigators find the car, they can compare items left at the crime scene (paint and glass) and an item removed from the crime scene (soil).

READING CHECKPOINT (SE p. 58) The PDQ contains test results for automotive paint samples.

Go Online

FOR Links on soil types
VISIT www.SciLinks.org
WEB CODE dan-1022

Students can download a worksheet that will guide their review of Internet sources on soil types.

Using Chromatography SE p. 60

Teach Key Concepts: Separating Mixtures

L3 **FOCUS** Tell students that a person is having a salad for lunch. It contains lettuce, tomatoes, ham, turkey, Swiss cheese, and hard-boiled eggs. The person also has a glass of iced tea with sugar and lemon juice added. **Q:** What do the salad and the iced tea have in common? **A:** They are both mixtures. **Q:** How are these mixtures different? **A:** The ingredients in the salad are visible and can be easily separated. The ingredients in the iced tea are not visible and are not as easily separated.

TEACH Explain that the mixtures forensic scientists separate are usually more like the tea than the salad. One tool that scientists use is chromatography. Display a strip of chromatography paper, a pen, and a beaker with a thin layer of water. **Q:** How can these items be used to separate the particles in ink? **A:** A drop of ink is placed on the paper. The end of the paper rests in the water. The water carries the ink up the paper.

Have students use the instructions in the Student Handbook to do either Part 2 of the Chapter 2 project or use those instructions to do another paper chromatography activity. When students have completed the activity, ask the following questions. **Q:** What happened to the ink? **A:** The pigments separated on the paper. **Q:** Why did some particles in ink move faster than other particles? **A:** There are different types of particles in ink with different properties, including size and the ability to dissolve in water. **Q:** Predict, in general, how the size of a particle will affect its speed. **A:** Larger (more massive) particles will tend to move more slowly than smaller particles.

L2 If students are having trouble understanding how the size (or the mass) of a particle could affect its speed, offer the following analogy. A person runs 5 miles in 40 minutes. Then the person runs the exact same course, but this time the person is wearing a 50-pound backpack. Ask students to predict how wearing the backpack will affect the runner's speed.

L4 Have students design a paper chromatography experiment to separate another liquid mixture, such as a fruit drink.

Background

MASS SPECTROMETRY Forensic chemists often combine gas chromatography with mass spectrometry. The chromatography products are allowed to flow into a mass spectrometer where they are bombarded with high-energy electrons. The result is a set of unstable charged particles (ions), which break down into smaller fragments. These smaller ions separate as they pass through an electric or magnetic field. The mass spectrometer produces a graph of the fragments that can be used to positively identify the substance.

Use Visuals: Figure 14

L3 **FOCUS** Tell students that Figure 14 shows the type of chromatography that could be used to analyze a paint chip from the hit-and-run in Figure 13.

TEACH Ask: **Q:** Why is it important that the gas used to carry the paint through the system doesn't react easily? **A:** *Sample answer:* If the gas could react easily with particles in the paint, substances that were not in the original sample would be detected and recorded. **Q:** Why do the particles move through the column at different speeds? **A:** Paint is a mixture of substances with different properties. **Q:** Based on the graph, what is the minimum number of substances in the paint? Why? **A:** There must be at least five substances because there are five peaks on the graph.

EL Have students make a list of terms in the diagram that are unfamiliar. Define and give examples of these terms.

L4 Ask students to compare paper and gas chromatography. **Q:** What are the samples being tested? **A:** ink; paint **Q:** What carries each sample through the system? **A:** water; a gas that does not react easily **Q:** How are the results displayed? **A:** as bands on paper; as peaks on a graph

Answers

FIGURE 14 The paint chip is heated to break down the paint into smaller substances that exist as gases at the temperature of the system.

Using Microscopes SE p. 61

Teaching Key Concepts: Microscopes Reveal Details

L3 **FOCUS** Explain that microscopes reveal details that can help a scientist identify a piece of evidence or compare two similar pieces of evidence.

TEACH Explain that some microscopes use light to reveal the details of an object and some use electrons. Photographs taken with an electron microscope are black and white; color is often added to these photos later. Use the photos of hairs on SE p. 56 and of pollen on p. 58 as examples of photos taken with a light microscope and an electron microscope.

APPLY Use Appendix B in the SE to discuss how a compound microscope works. Then refer students to the comparison microscope in Figure 15. Point out the single eyepiece and the two stages where the samples are placed. You can preview the photograph on SE p. 67 to show how the comparison microscope is used.

L1 Supervise visually impaired students as they use their sense of touch to identify the parts of a microscope.

L2 Use the Building Science Vocabulary worksheet on Greek word origins in the Student Handbook.

Answers

READING CHECKPOINT (SE p. 61) The SEM uses a stream of electrons.

Assess

Reviewing Key Concepts

1. **a.** small amounts of evidence left at a crime scene
   b. *Sample answer:* Tweezers could be used to pick up a paint chip. A forensic vacuum cleaner could be used to collect soil from an imprint.
   c. *Sample answer:* A CSI would look for shoe prints, tool marks, and broken glass.
2. **a.** *Sample answers:* natural: wool, cotton; synthetic: nylon, polyester
   b. *Sample answer:* no, because many people have hair with a similar structure
   c. *Sample answer:* Evidence that is brought to a crime scene is generally more useful because it may be connected to objects in a suspect's home.
3. **a.** Most trace evidence is a mixture that must be separated before it can be identified. Chromatography can be used to separate mixtures based on their properties.
   b. They can see details of evidence that are not visible to the unaided eye.

Reteach

L2 Divide students into small groups. Have each student take a turn asking the other students questions about the lesson.

Performance Assessment

L3 **WRITING** Tell students that a driver speeding on a wet road loses control of his car. The speeding car hits a car in the next lane. The second car crashes into a tree. The driver of the second car is injured. The first driver does not stop. Have students write a paragraph explaining how investigators could use paint chips found at the scene to locate the car. Remind students to include information about technology the investigators might use.

L4 **SKILLS CHECK** Ask students to compare and contrast what a scientist might do to analyze a hair sample with what a scientist might do to analyze a soil sample.

At-Home Activity: Collecting Trace Evidence

Remind students not to use a car that was recently cleaned. If students do not have access to a car, they could do a similar activity with a sofa, a desk drawer, or any other object in which trace evidence is likely to be lurking.

Chapter Project

KEEP STUDENTS ON TRACK By now, students should have analyzed the ink from the ransom note. They should have compared the results to the tests done on ink from the three pen brands and used the data to narrow their list of suspects.

Forensics & Physical Science

Arson Investigations SE pp. 62–63

Background Once a fire is under control, investigators begin to search the scene. They usually search from the least damaged areas toward the area with the greatest damage. Most often, the place where the fire started has the most damage. Along the way, they look for clues such as charred wood, smoke damage, and glazed glass.

Researchers set fires under controlled conditions to provide scientific data to support arson investigations and prosecutions. Researchers have discovered that two variables have a major effect on fire patterns—ventilation and flashover. A flashover occurs when heat builds up in a room and the upper portions of the room burst into flame. The research results may challenge accepted wisdom. For example, a flashover can produce a fire pattern that resembles the pattern produced by an accelerant.

Teach Key Concepts

THE FIRE TRIANGLE

FOCUS Tell students that firefighters use different methods to extinguish fires. Each method attacks at least one factor in the fire triangle—fuel, oxygen, or heat.

TEACH Present examples of firefighting methods and ask students to identify the factor being targeted. Examples: Water from hoses targets heat; foam from a fire extinguisher targets oxygen; making a firebreak in front of an advancing forest fire targets fuel.

Go Online

FOR Links on fire triangle
VISIT www.SciLinks.org
WEB CODE dan-1020

Download a worksheet for students.

At-Home Activity

FIRE SAFETY

Tell students that knowing what to do in case of fire can save lives. Review the rules and routes for leaving the school building if a fire alarm sounds. Then encourage students to talk with their families about what to do at home in case of a fire. Suggest that they agree on a plan and have a practice drill.

Help Students Read

BUILDING VOCABULARY

Explain that the adjective *flammable* (able to flame) is used to describe materials that burn easily. Ask students what adding the prefix *non-* to *flammable* will do.

Explain that *accelerate* means "to speed up." Use the example of the accelerator, or gas pedal, on a car. Explain that an accelerant is used to speed up a combustion reaction.

In the Community

INVITE A GUEST SPEAKER

Contact your local fire department and ask if there is someone who would be qualified and willing to come speak with your class about arson investigations. If you live in or near a big city, that city might have a fire marshal. If you are truly fortunate, you may be able to arrange a visit from an investigator and his or her canine partner. Let your guest know what the students have been studying and what they have learned about arson. Have students prepare questions in advance.

You Be the Judge

1. The foam prevents oxygen from reaching the fuel.
2. The lighter fluid acts as an accelerant.
3. *Sample answers:* Taxpayers have to pay for fighting fires and investigating suspicious fires. Burnt-out buildings lower the value of property in a neighborhood and may provide havens for illegal activities.

Identifying Firearms

Reading Preview

OBJECTIVES

After this lesson, students will be able to

2.3.1 Compare the types of evidence that investigators collect when a weapon is fired.

2.3.2 Summarize the methods used to analyze evidence from firearms.

KEY TERMS

• cartridge • rifling • gunshot residue

Target Reading Skill: Relating Cause and Effect

Explain that a cause makes something happen. An effect is what happens. When students recognize that one event causes another, they are relating cause and effect. Explain that a cause can have more than one effect.

SAMPLE ANSWERS

Students may include the following answers.

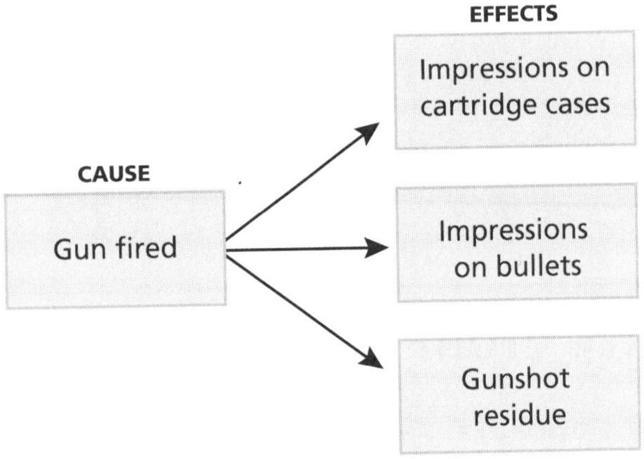

DIFFERENTIATED INSTRUCTION KEY

Use this key as you review the instructional strategies.

- L1 For students with special needs
- L2 For less proficient readers
- L3 For all students
- L4 For gifted and talented students
- EL For English language learners

Preteach

Build Background Knowledge: Using Prior Knowledge

Tell students that firing a weapon leaves both prints and trace evidence. Ask students to predict what that evidence might be, based on books they have read or movies and television shows they have seen.

Discover Activity Where Does the Powder Go? SE p. 64

SKILLS FOCUS Making Models

TIME 20 minutes

TEAM SIZE small group

MATERIALS plastic spoon, funnel, cornstarch, small balloon, pin

TIPS Make sure the volunteers are wearing goggles and an apron or lab coat. Have one student blow up the balloon a few times so it will easily inflate after the cornstarch is added. You want the balloon almost at its maximum diameter to produce the air pressure needed to propel the cornstarch once the balloon is burst.

For the best simulation, have the student with the pin stand directly in front of the student who is holding the balloon. If you are uncomfortable with such an obvious attacker and victim arrangement, adjust the positions. You may want to place black construction paper on the floor so that the pattern of residue will be more visible.

EXPECTED OUTCOME The cornstarch will be scattered, but some will land on the hand of the person holding the balloon.

THINK IT OVER Students' drawings should include all locations where the cornstarch landed.

Instruct

Evidence From Firearms SE pp. 65–66

Teach Key Concepts: Fired Weapons Leave Evidence

L3 **FOCUS** Ask students if they have ever played or watched people play paintball. **Q:** What is the object of this activity? **A:** to score hits and eliminate players from the game **Q:** How do observers know when a player has been hit? **A:** Paint is left on the person's clothing around the point of impact. Explain that the act of shooting an object at high speed toward a target always leaves some evidence.

TEACH Before class, make a black-and-white copy of SE p. 65. Cut out the drawing in Figure 16. Tape the image in the center of a plain white sheet of paper. Orient the image so there is as much white space as possible around the image. Then make copies of the page. Have students work in small groups. Ask the students to use the text on SE pp. 65–66 to find the purpose of each of the following items—trigger, firing pin, cartridge, bullet, primer, gunpowder, barrel, and rifling. They should record the results on their papers. Then ask students to infer the purpose of the hammer, safety, and ejector mechanism.

APPLY Ask students to relate the design and operation of a gun to the evidence that is produced when the gun is fired.

L1 For visually impaired students, obtain a piece of galvanized pipe with female threads from your school maintenance department or a hardware store. A pipe cap or coupling will work. Choose a pipe diameter that will allow a student to feel the grooves inside the pipe.

L2 Have students draw a flowchart showing, step by step, what happens when a person pulls the trigger on a loaded gun.

Chapter 2

Background

FIREARMS EVIDENCE The purpose of the spiral grooves, or rifling, in modern handguns and rifles is to improve the accuracy of the weapon. Ironically, a feature that makes modern weapons so accurate produces significant evidence that can be used to link a gun to a crime. Manufacturers specify the pattern of grooves for a given model. But during the manufacturing process, scratches, scrapes, nicks, and other flaws are introduced into each barrel. These variations produce the striations on a bullet.

Gunpowder residue is not the only trace evidence from firearms. Gun owners clean and oil their weapons to keep them in firing condition. Handling the gun or the bullets can leave oily traces on the hands. In addition, there may be tiny metal traces left when ammunition is loaded.

Address Misconceptions: Hardness of a Bullet

FOCUS Most students think that a bullet is made of an extremely hard material. They may wonder how it is possible for a gun barrel to make grooves and scratches on a bullet.

TEACH One way to measure the hardness of a material is to try to scratch the material with materials of known hardness. Explain that lead is a relatively soft metal—about 1.5 on the Mohs hardness scale. The steel used to make gun barrels is much harder than lead.

APPLY Explain that bullets often have a thin brass coating called a jacket. Ask students to predict whether brass is harder or softer than steel, and to give a reason for their answer. (Brass is softer because the rifling in a gun barrel leaves grooves and scratches on the surface of a jacketed bullet.)

Skills Activity Making Models SE p. 66

TIME 15 minutes

TEAM SIZE pair

MATERIALS wide plastic straw, scissors, pin, clay, cotton swab

TIPS Wrap tape around one end of the swab and trim the tape to keep the cotton from sticking to the clay. Have the students knead the clay to make it more pliable.

EXPECTED OUTCOME There should be a pattern of grooves in the clay that reflect the projections that were produced when the students made pinholes in the straw. Students should be able to compare this result with the marks made when a bullet is forced past the rifling in a gun barrel.

Answers

FIGURE 16 The cartridge is ejected.

READING CHECKPOINT (SE p. 66) the spiral grooves inside the barrel (rifling)

Analyzing Firearms Evidence SE pp. 67–68

Teach Key Concepts: Comparing Firearms Evidence

L3 **FOCUS** Explain that some of the methods that analysts use with other types of print evidence work with the prints left on bullets.

TEACH Tell students that the crime lab has bullets from a murder victim and cartridge cases from the crime scene. **Q:** How can a firearms analyst use this evidence to determine the type of gun that was used? **A:** The analyst looks for marks on the cartridge cases and the rifling pattern on the bullet.

Tell students that a detective has identified a suspect. **Q:** What should the detective do next? **A:** The detective should get a search warrant for the suspect's home (or other property). **Q:** If the right type of gun is found during a search, what will happen next? **A:** The gun is test fired to obtain a bullet and cartridge case for comparison. **Q:** What happens next? **A:** The analyst uses a comparison microscope to see if the scratches on the bullets and cartridge cases line up.

APPLY Tell students that the crime lab has bullets from a murder victim and cartridge cases from the crime scene, but detectives do not have a suspect. **Q:** Is there another way to locate the gun used in the crime? **A:** Scan images of a bullet and cartridge case. Then do a search in a database of firearms evidence.

L1 Use a utility blade and linoleum blocks to model the scratch marks on a bullet. Prepare three samples with different patterns of horizontal cuts. Then cut each block in half. Have students use visual or tactile observations to match up the correct halves.

L4 Tell students that a suspect is identified and located within hours of the murder. Have students explain why a CSI might use both a swab and tape to collect gunshot residue from the suspect. (A scanning electron microscope can be used to observe the particles of residue collected with tape. The residue on swabs is used in chemical tests that can identify trace elements.)

Background

FIREARMS DATABASES In 1992 the FBI began using DRUGFIRE, which allowed the FBI to store and link data about ammunition. Unfortunately, DRUGFIRE was not compatible with the image analysis system being used by the Bureau of Alcohol, Tobacco, and Firearms (ATF). They were using a system called the Integrated Ballistic Identification System, or IBIS. By 1997, the agencies realized that they could not make the two competing systems work together. They agreed to jointly develop a National Integrated Ballistics Information Network (NIBIN), which connects all the IBIS databases.

STOLEN GUNS When a gun used in a crime is traced back to the registered owner, the owner may claim that the gun had been stolen. It is difficult for the police to refute the claim. As of 2007, Connecticut, Massachusetts, Michigan, New York, Ohio, and Rhode Island had passed laws to address this problem. These laws require gun owners to report a lost or stolen gun promptly. For a first infraction, the owner is fined. Subsequent failures to report a stolen gun carry larger fines and a possible prison sentence.

Answers

FIGURE 18 The bullets in Comparison A were fired from the same gun because the scratches on the bullets line up when the bullets are viewed through a comparison microscope.

READING CHECKPOINT (SE p. 68) The images in a firearms database include evidence from crime scenes and test firings.

Assess

Reviewing Key Concepts

1. a. Leftover powder that sprays out of the trigger hole ends up on a shooter's hands.
   b. Both types of marks are impressions. Marks left by rifling can be used to identify a class of gun. Marks left by flaws can be used to identify a specific gun.
   c. The locations of bullets and cartridge cases can help show where the shooter was when the gun was fired.
2. a. A firearms expert can look at the residue particles with a scanning electron microscope or do chemical tests to identify traces of lead, antimony, and barium in the residue.
   b. Sequence: Test fire the gun; compare the rifling on the test bullet to a bullet from the crime scene; use a comparison microscope to compare the pattern of scratches on the bullets.
   c. *Sample answer:* Searches can be done quickly; each lab has more data to compare with its data.

Reteach

L2 Have students look at Figure 18 on SE p. 67. Ask questions such as the following. What causes scratches on the bullets? How do these scratches help investigators solve crimes? What is the advantage of observing bullets with a comparison microscope?

Performance Assessment

L3 **WRITING** Have students work in pairs to prepare a training guide for a firearms analyst. Ask them to include information about collecting and testing different types of firearms evidence.

L2 **SKILLS CHECK** Have students explain why a lesson about identifying firearms was included in a chapter called "Prints and Trace Evidence."

In the Community: Reducing Crime

Buy-back programs are often greeted with enthusiasm by communities, but the money allotted usually is not sufficient to significantly reduce the percentage of gun ownership. Opponents argue that these programs do not remove guns from criminals. They also argue that people with multiple guns keep at least one. Proponents argue that removing any gun can prevent a suicide by firearm or an accidental shooting.

Chapter 2

Chapter Review

Study Guide SE p. 69

Apply the Big Idea

Connect to Key Concepts
Reinforce the chapter's Big Idea by connecting it to important Key Concepts. For example, ask, "Why do investigators look for prints made by objects that leave a distinctive pattern?" (These patterns can be used to connect a print to the object that made the print.) How can a database of prints help solve a crime? (Print examiners can use a database to identify the make and model of the shoe or tire that left a print at a crime scene.)

Connecting Key Terms
Reinforce the chapter's Big Idea by asking students to make a connection between pairs of Key Terms. For example, if you pair *microscope* with *gunshot residue,* students could say that some particles in gunshot residue have distinctive shapes that are visible when viewed with a scanning electron microscope. If you pair *classifying* with *trace evidence,* students could say that sorting trace evidence into groups is an example of classifying.

Review and Assessment SE pp. 70–71

Organizing Information

a. impressions **b.** database of images
c. taking photographs **d.** making casts

Reviewing Key Terms

1. b **2.** c **3.** d **4.** a **5.** c
6. False; skid marks **7.** True
8. True **9.** False; a microscope
10. False; cartridge

Writing in Science

WRITING MODE: Instructions

SCORING RUBRIC

4	Exceeds criteria: Well-written; the instructions are clear, accurate, and presented in a logical order.
3	Meets criteria: The student has included all the necessary instructions for recording and collecting both types of evidence.
2	The instructions are incomplete.
1	The instructions are not accurate.

Checking Concepts

11. Imprints are flat and two-dimensional; impressions have three dimensions—width, length, and depth.
12. shoe size and width, sole pattern, uneven wear, distinctive cuts or marks
13. Touching the mark can alter it and destroy its value as evidence.
14. take photographs, make casts, remove objects from a crime scene
15. hair, fiber, glass, paint, soil
16. Images of the samples are shown side by side, which makes comparisons easier.
17. impressions on cartridge cases and bullets; gunshot residue

Thinking Critically

18. *Sample answer:* The orange sole has a wider central groove, one more cross-hatch, and one more circle than the blue sole does.
19. They might infer that the driver didn't use the brakes to try to stop the car.
20. The exam can eliminate suspects and it can help a scientist decide whether to do more expensive tests.
21. Students can conclude that the gun was used because rifling and scratches can link a bullet to a specific weapon. Without other evidence, such as gunshot residue, students cannot conclude that Mr. Green fired the gun.

Applying Skills

22. skid marks
23. soil from the crime scene
24. The investigator could estimate how fast the car was traveling.
25. They can see if the glass particles fit cracks in the headlight. They can test to see if the composition of the glass in the headlight and the glass at the crime scene is the same.
26. Paint from an undamaged area would be an exact or a close match to a paint chip left at the crime scene. A sample taken from the damaged area could contain paint transferred from another vehicle during the collision.

Chapter Project

PERFORMANCE ASSESSMENT Students should have completed both parts of the project. Their reports should include their test results and an explanation of how they used the results to narrow the list of possible suspects.

Chapter 3

Identifying an Individual

Chapter at a Glance SE pp. 72–103

		Resources
Project	Identifying the Thief	• Chapter Project Worksheet
Lesson 1	**Fingerprints** 3.1.1 Distinguish patterns used to describe fingerprints. 3.1.2 Compare methods used to collect latent prints. 3.1.3 Explain how examiners analyze the prints found at a crime scene	• Vocabulary Worksheet • Reading and Note Taking Guide 3-1 • Laboratory Investigation 8: Latent Clues • Video Viewing Guide 3 • Video: Fingerprint Evidence
Lesson 2	**Evidence From Blood** 3.2.1 Describe the methods used to detect blood. 3.2.2 Explain how blood is classified. 3.2.3 Interpret patterns of bloodstains.	• Reading and Note Taking Guide 3-2 • Laboratory Investigation 9: Every Drop Tells a Story • Video: Clues From Bloodstains • SciLinks: blood type
	Forensics & Life Science Facial Reconstruction	• SciLinks: animal symmetry
Lesson 3	**DNA Evidence** 3.3.1 State the reason for DNA's value as a tool for forensic scientists. 3.3.2 Summarize the process for making a DNA profile. 3.3.3 Explain why DNA profiles are accepted as evidence. 3.3.4 Describe the uses of DNA profiles.	• Reading and Note Taking Guide 3-3 • Laboratory Investigation 10: The Power of DNA Evidence • Video: DNA to the Rescue • SciLinks: DNA fingerprinting
Lesson 4	**Handwriting and Voice Identification** 3.4.1 Identify clues used to compare writing samples. 3.4.2 Describe the methods analysts use to compare voice samples.	• Reading and Note Taking Guide 3-4 • Skills Lab Worksheet • Video: Voice Stress Analysis
Review and Assessment		• Chapter 3 Test

Chapter Activities Planner

Activity/Time	Inquiry	Team Size/Materials	Skills
Chapter Project 45 minutes	Guided	Team Size: small group blood-typing tray, fake blood, fake Anti-A and Anti-B sera, toothpicks, clock or stopwatch, hand lens	observing, inferring, drawing conclusions
Lesson 1			
Discover Activity 10 minutes	Directed	Team Size: individual washable marker, facial tissue, hand lens	developing hypotheses
Skills Activity 30 minutes	Guided	Team Size: pair ink pad with washable ink, sheets of white paper, glass with latent print, talcum powder, transparent tape (optional)	classifying
At-Home Activity 25 minutes	Open-ended	Team Size: small group soft pencil or ink pad with washable ink, index cards	classifying, communicating
Lesson 2			
Discover Activity 10 minutes	Guided	Team Size: small group large white paper, fake blood, metric ruler	predicting
Skills Activity 10 minutes	Guided	Team size: individual	interpreting data
Lesson 3			
Discover Activity 15 minutes	Directed	Team Size: individual snap cubes in three different colors	interpreting data
Skills Activity 10 minutes	Guided	Team Size: pair partial bar code and sheet of complete bar codes	drawing conclusions
Lesson 4			
Discover Activity 15 minutes	Open-ended	Team Size: individual multiple signatures on a sheet of paper, hand lens	inferring
Skills Activity 10 minutes	Directed	Team Size: class recording of voices	observing
Skills Lab 45 minutes	Directed	Team Size: individual ruled paper, metric ruler, protractor, tracing paper	measuring, calculating, designing experiments

Chapter 3

Identifying an Individual

From the Author

Your students may have had their fingerprints recorded as part of a local public safety initiative. If so, your students have seen firsthand one of the most important tools of law enforcement. Unlike the prints discussed in Chapter 2, fingerprints can be used to make a positive identification. But the process isn't foolproof. For example, the prints at a crime scene may be only partial prints or they may be blurred. Thus, deciding whether a print from a crime scene matches a suspect's print isn't as easy as it might seem. Two print examiners looking at the same prints might not reach the same conclusion.

The methods scientists developed to study DNA have had a profound effect on forensic science. Now law enforcement has the perfect tool for positively identifying a suspect—barring human error in the collection and processing of the biological samples. It can be challenging to present up-to-date information about DNA profiles. In most crime labs, a replicate-and-sort method has replaced the traditional cut-and-sort method. Graphs similar to graphs from gas chromatography have replaced the familiar banded gels. You will have to determine how deeply to delve into the details with your students.

Background

FINGERPRINTS By the early 1900s, police departments in the United States had accepted fingerprints as a reliable method for connecting an individual to a crime scene. This method has three advantages. Every fingerprint has a unique pattern of ridges. The pattern remains unchanged throughout a person's life. Fingerprints share general characteristics that can be used to establish a classification system.

As described in the textbook, analysis of fingerprints occurs at three levels—general features, finer details, and small variations (also known as "minutiae"). When comparing prints, the examiner needs to find a minimum of 12 points of similarity at the third level. If an examiner decides that there is a match between two prints, a second examiner must verify the match.

TESTING FOR BLOOD From the tests done to identify blood at a crime scene, a CSI can presume that a sample is blood. But tests must be done at the crime lab to confirm that the sample is blood and that it is human blood. If human blood is injected into a rabbit, antigens in the blood will cause the rabbit to produce antibodies. Blood from the rabbit is then used to make an antiserum—a blood serum containing antibodies. Some of the sample from the crime scene is placed in a test tube over a layer of the antiserum. If clumps form where the samples meet, the sample is human blood. The test is called a *precipitin* test.

An antiserum can be produced for other species in a similar way. There are antisera for animals, such as cats and dogs.

DNA PROFILES A biological sample collected from a crime scene may be old or may have been exposed to heat, light, moisture, or mold. These conditions can cause DNA to degrade. Some segments of non-coding DNA are relatively stable because they are short (less than 450 bases). These short tandem repeats, or STRs, are good candidates for multiplication because there is less chance for errors to be introduced during replication.

One multiplication method uses a three-step cycle. (1) The mixture is heated and the DNA molecules unwind. (2) The mixture is cooled and primers bond to the single strands. Primers are fragments of DNA that attach to bases on either side of an STR and mark off the area to be copied. (3) The mixture is heated, nitrogen bases fill in the sequences between the primers, and the molecule rewinds.

Chapter 3

Focus on the Big Idea

Use the Big Idea question as a way to activate prior knowledge.

PRESENT THE IDEA Read aloud the Big Idea question. Explain that every person has a combination of traits that make that person unique, or one of a kind. But what forensic scientists need are single traits that can vary from person to person. They also need traits that can be measured.

DISCUSSION QUESTIONS Then ask the following questions. **Q:** Why can't scientists use hair color, eye color, or height to identify an individual? **A:** Many people have the same hair color, eye color, or height. **Q:** What is one trait scientists do use to identify an individual? **A:** Students are likely to know that fingerprints are unique.

FOLLOW UP See the Teach the Big Idea instruction strategy on TG p. 93.

Forensic Science Videos Video Viewing Guide 3

Discovery EDUCATION

VIDEO Fingerprint Evidence

TIME 4:15 minutes

DESCRIPTION This video provides a general introduction to the collection and analysis of fingerprint evidence.

TEACHING TIPS You could use this video to introduce the lesson or to provide support for your less proficient readers.

VIDEO Clues From Bloodstains

TIME 4:30 minutes

DESCRIPTION This video shows how police learn to interpret bloodstain patterns.

TEACHING TIPS You can use this video to extend the discussion in the textbook.

VIDEO DNA to the Rescue

TIME 4:23 minutes

DESCRIPTION This video presents a case in which DNA was used to free a person who was wrongly convicted.

TEACHING TIPS You can use this video to reinforce the limits of hair as evidence as compared to DNA evidence.

VIDEO Voice Stress Analysis

TIME 5:59 minutes

DESCRIPTION This video shows how voice stress can be used as an indicator of truthfulness.

TEACHING TIPS Discuss other clues, such as eye movements, that interviewers use to judge the reliability of answers.

Chapter 3 Project SE p. 73

Identifying the Thief

SKILLS OBJECTIVES

After this activity, students will be able to

- use ABO blood typing to identify the blood type of an unknown sample
- use the results of blood typing to narrow a list of suspects

TEACHING TIP Do this activity after students complete Lesson 2.

CLASS TIME 45 minutes

TEAM SIZE 5–6 students

MATERIALS fake crime scene blood samples, labeled CS-1, CS-2, CS-3, and CS-4; fake antisera

SAFETY

Students should wear goggles, a lab apron, and plastic gloves. They should clean up all spills immediately and wash their hands thoroughly with soap after the activity.

Reassure students that the liquids they will be using are nonbiological and do not contain any harmful bacteria or viruses. That is why the word *fake* is used in the materials list to describe the blood and the antisera.

BEGIN THE PROJECT Review the material about classifying blood on SE pages 82–83, especially the information on blood typing in Figure 6. Make sure students understand that blood typing can be used to eliminate a suspect or to narrow a list of suspects. Blood typing cannot, however, be used to positively identify a suspect. Then tell students that the crime lab collected the blood that was left at the crime scene by the thief. The fake blood that they test will provide the same test results as the blood that was collected at the crime scene.

TEACHING TIPS Do not tell students that there are four different types of fake blood. Place masking tape over the labels on the bottles before you distribute the samples so students will not know which type of blood is in the bottle. Distribute at least one sample of each type of blood.

If students are having trouble observing the clumping of the blood, have one team member carefully hold the tray about 12 cm above a sheet of white paper. Then, have other team members use a hand lens to view the mixture under low magnification and then under higher magnification.

If you have the Motic® digital camera and software, use the setup described in Laboratory Investigation 7 to show students what clumping in fake blood looks like.

EXPECTED OUTCOME Students should determine the blood type of the sample they receive. Then, students should use their results and the list of suspects they compiled while doing the Chapter 2 project to identify the thief.

DISPOSAL Clean up spills and thoroughly wash equipment with soap and water. You can discard disposable items in the trash.

Alternative Crime Scene

If there is any evidence from the crime scene or from the suspects that was not tested in Chapter 2, have students test and compare this evidence. The test results should allow students to identify the thief.

Fingerprints

Reading Preview

OBJECTIVES

After this lesson, students will be able to

3.1.1 Distinguish patterns used to describe fingerprints.
3.1.2 Compare methods used to collect latent prints.
3.1.3 Explain how examiners analyze the prints found at a crime scene.

KEY TERMS

• ridge • visible print • plastic print • latent print

Target Reading Skill: Asking Questions

Remind students that asking questions can provide a framework for reading. For example, turning headings into questions can help students focus on important information as they read.

SAMPLE ANSWERS

Students may include the following answers.

FINGERPRINTS

Q. How are fingerprints described?
A. Ridge line patterns are used to describe fingerprints.
Q. How are fingerprints collected?
A. Fingerprints are revealed by dusting, lighting, or chemical reactions. Tape is used to "lift" the prints.
Q. How are fingerprints identified?
A. Fingerprint examiners try to match the prints with prints from a suspect or prints in a database.

DIFFERENTIATED INSTRUCTION KEY

Use this key as you review the instructional strategies.

L1 For students with special needs
L2 For less proficient readers
L3 For all students
L4 For gifted and talented students
EL For English language learners

Preteach

Build Background Knowledge: Ridges

L3 Revisit the illustration of a tire tread on SE p. 46. Review why most tires have a rib-and-groove design. Stress that the ribs help the tires grip a road surface. Then explain that there are areas on their fingertips that are similar to ribs. These slightly raised areas are called ridges. They make it easier to grasp and hold onto objects.

L2 Review the general meaning of the term *ridge*—a long narrow raised area. Then discuss other examples of ridges. One example is a narrow elevation of land on Earth's surface or on the ocean floor.

L1 Circulate a swatch of ribbed fabric and let students feel the raised cords.

Discover Activity — What Can You See on a Fingertip? SE p. 74

SKILLS FOCUS Developing Hypotheses

TIME 10 minutes

TEAM SIZE individual

MATERIALS washable marker, facial tissue, hand lens

TIPS Do not use permanent markers. Have students wash off the color as soon as they complete the activity. Have a range of colors to accommodate variations in palm skin tones.

EXPECTED OUTCOME The drawings should show the pattern formed by ridges on their finger.

THINK IT OVER Students should infer that the lines on a fingerprint are produced by the ridges on a fingertip.

Instruct

Describing Fingerprints SE p. 75

Teach Key Concepts: Fingerprints Have Patterns

L3 **FOCUS** Explain that no two people have the same fingerprints. But fingerprints do share characteristics that can be used to classify them into groups.

TEACH Use Figure 1 on SE p. 75 to discuss the differences between loops, whorls, and arches. After students look at the labeled drawing, ask them to find examples of a fork, ridge ending, dot, and enclosure on the prints.

APPLY Have students use an ink pad with washable ink to make a print of the index finger on their right hand. They should roll the inked finger from left to right in the center of a sheet of unlined paper. Ask students to identify the general pattern and record this information on their paper. Have students circle and label a few details that might be used to distinguish the print from other prints with a similar pattern.

As a class, determine how many students have each fingerprint pattern. Then calculate the percentage of each type. Do the data support the information in the textbook about loops being the most common and arches being the least common? If not, have students suggest a reason why this might be so. (Size of sample is one possible reason.)

If you plan to do the Skills Activity on SE p. 79, draw lines to divide two sheets of unlined paper into 16 squares each. Have students make a second print of their right index finger in a square and initial the square.

EL Ask students to draw and label a simple loop, whorl, and arch pattern. Then ask them to think of objects that have these shapes. Jewelry, ropes, or embroidery can have loops. Some windows, doorways, and bridges have arches. For whorls, consider shells, a coiled garden hose, or clouds in a hurricane.

L1 Ask for volunteers to help you make 3-D models of the patterns for visually impaired students. These could be simple (a coil of wires for a whorl pattern) or more elaborate (pipe cleaners bent into shapes and glued to cardboard). Make sure the models can be handled without causing injury.

L4 Have students prepare a report on the subcategories of print patterns. For example, a loop can be classified as a radial loop if the loop opens toward the thumb; it can be classified as an ulnar loop if the loop opens toward the little finger. Students could use the information to further classify their prints.

Chapter 3

Answers

READING CHECKPOINT (SE p. 75) raised lines on fingertips

FIGURE 1 A fork is a point where a ridge splits. An enclosure is a point where a ridge splits and joins up again.

Collecting Fingerprints SE pp. 76–77

Teach Key Concepts: Revealing Latent Fingerprints

L3 **FOCUS** Ask students if they have held a drinking glass up to the light and noticed smudges on the glass that they had not noticed before. Explain that most fingerprints at a crime scene won't be immediately noticeable.

TEACH Explain that there are glands beneath the surface of the skin that produce sweat, which contains mainly water and salt, and other substances such as lipids (fats). Sweat travels through ducts to the surface of the skin and is released through small openings called pores. When sweat is transferred to a surface, the print that is left is not visible. To reveal these invisible, or latent, prints, a CSI can dust with a powder that will cling to the ridge patterns left by the sweat. The CSI can also use chemicals that react with chemicals in sweat.

APPLY Have students do Part 1 of Laboratory Investigation 8 in the Student Handbook.

L1 Have students make prints in finger paint and soft wax as examples of visible and plastic prints.

L4 Have students make a list of surfaces in your classroom where a CSI might find latent prints. (Possible surfaces are handles on doors and drawers; desktops or chair backs; books; beakers and graduated cylinders.) For each surface, ask students to describe the surface and identify the method that a CSI might use to collect the prints.

Use Visuals: Figure 2

L3 **FOCUS** Explain that the visuals show examples of ways to reveal latent prints. The last photo shows a print being lifted with transparent tape.

TEACH Have students compare the photos of the wand and banana with the photo of the police officer using dusting powder. Explain that the powder used with a magnetic wand contains tiny bits of iron, which are attracted to a magnet. Magnetic powder works better than regular dusting powder on porous surfaces or on multicolored surfaces. Another advantage of a magnetic wand is its ability to remove excess powder from a print without damaging the print. (By changing the position of the magnet in the wand, a CSI can release the excess powder from the wand into a storage container.)

Use the photos of the handprint and the print on the foil to discuss the role that lighting and chemical reactions play in revealing prints. Note that a chemical method, such as fuming, may be followed by dusting so that the revealed print can be lifted with tape.

Tell students that with chemical methods, there is a risk that a print will be damaged. Also, some methods won't work if another method is tried first. So a technician photographs the prints revealed by one method before trying another method.

L1 Visually impaired students could use a hand lens to view the details in the photographs of the print on the banana and the print on the foil.

Help Students Read: Visualizing

L2 Ask students to imagine walking into a room that contains a print on a wall, a plastic print in melted candle wax, and latent prints on a magazine. Ask students to close their eyes, visualize each example, and describe what they see.

EL Have students make a list of unfamiliar words in this section. Have them work with a partner to make a glossary that contains definitions and drawings that will help them remember the meanings of these words. For example, students could draw a pot of water with a flame below to represent the presence of *vapor*. They could draw a sponge to represent *porous*.

Monitor Progress

L2 **WRITING** Have students describe the three types of fingerprints that may be found at a crime scene.

L3 **WRITING** Ask students to describe the best method for recovering prints from a doorknob, an apple, a cardboard box, and a leather wallet.

Answers

FIGURE 2 A dark powder will show up better on a clear glass surface.

READING CHECKPOINT (SE p. 77) A porous surface has tiny holes, or pores, that can absorb materials such as sweat and oil.

Identifying Fingerprints SE pp. 78–79

Teach Key Concepts: Comparing Prints

L3 **FOCUS** Point out that once fingerprints are collected, they need to be identified.

TEACH Discuss how examiners get prints to compare with prints from a crime scene. **Q:** In general, what do examiners need to identify an unknown print from a crime scene? **A:** They need known prints to compare to the unknown print. **Q:** Why would police officers collect prints from people who are not suspects? **A:** They want to eliminate some unknown prints as evidence. **Q:** How do police officers collect prints from a person? **A:** They use an ink pad and a fingerprint card or they use a scanner.

Explain the three levels of review that an examiner does on a print—ridge patterns, details, and small variations. Then discuss how a computer database can help to identify a print. **Q:** What are the advantages of using a fingerprint database? **A:** The process of comparing prints is faster and the examiner has more data. **Q:** What is the examiner's role when the examiner uses an automated system? **A:** The examiner must decide if any of the prints supplied by the computer is a good match for the unknown print.

APPLY Ask students to imagine that someone stole some money from a safe in a home. A CSI comes to collect evidence. **Q:** Whose fingerprints would the CSI expect to find on the safe? **A:** the owner of the safe **Q:** Why would the CSI collect prints from the owner? **A:** to eliminate any prints left by the owner from evidence **Q:** What will the print examiner do with prints that remain after the owner's prints are eliminated? **A:** The examiner will scan the prints and use a computer to look for likely matches. Then have students do Part 2 of Laboratory Investigation 8 in the Student Handbook.

L2 Have students review how print examiners use a database of shoe prints. Ask students to compare and contrast using a shoe print database with using a fingerprint database.

EL Make sure that students know what a scanner is. Explain that the scanner functions as a camera, taking a picture of the ridge patterns on a finger. The scanner has a light source that highlights the ridges, which appear as dark lines in the image.

L4 Ask students to research and report on uses for the FBI database other than identifying prints found at a crime scene. (The database is used to check if people applying for certain jobs, such as a security guard, have a criminal record. It is also used to do a background check on people who want to purchase a gun.)

Skills Activity Classifying SE p. 79

TIME 30 minutes

TEAM SIZE pair

MATERIALS ink pad with washable ink, sheets of white paper; glass with latent print, talcum powder, transparent tape (optional)

L3 TIPS Draw lines to divide two sheets of unlined paper into 16 squares each. Have students make a print of their right index finger in a square and initial the square. Make copies of the print database for each pair of students.

EXPECTED OUTCOME Students should be able to find at least one detail on each print in their largest group to distinguish each print from the others. This exercise reinforces the concept that fingerprints are unique.

EXTENSION Before class, have one student leave a latent print of his or her right index finger on a pocket mirror or other hard, flat surface. During class, sprinkle talcum powder over the print. Shake off any excess powder. Place a piece of transparent tape over the print, rub the tape gently to remove any bubbles, and lift the print from the glass. Place the tape on a piece of paper. Then make a copy of the paper for each team and ask students to use their database to identify the print.

L1 Provide hand lenses for visually impaired students.

Address Misconceptions: Use of Technology

FOCUS Students may think that technology is used to try and solve every reported crime.

TEACH Explain that law enforcement agencies do not have unlimited amounts of time and money. Crime labs often have backlogs of evidence waiting to be analyzed. Serious crimes, such as murder, will get more resources. Detectives also need to determine if using technology will help solve a crime.

APPLY Present the following situations. A thief breaks into a car and steals a laptop computer. A thief breaks into a school and steals 15 computers from the computer lab. Investigators find a half-empty can of cola in the lab. Ask students to predict whether investigators will dust for prints in the car or in the lab to solve the crime. Have students give a reason for their prediction. (Investigators are likely to collect prints at the school because the thief probably left a print on the can. Investigators probably won't collect prints from the car because they would need to eliminate many prints to find any print left by the thief.)

FYI The admissibility of fingerprints as evidence was first established in 1911 in the case of *People* v. *Jennings.* Fingerprints that were left on a freshly painted railing were used to convict Jennings of murder.

Answers

FIGURE 4 Although the overall patterns are similar, when students examine the details, they should conclude that Fingerprint A is a better match.

Assess

Reviewing Key Concepts

1. **a.** loops, whorls, and arches
   b. whorl
   c. No two people, even identical twins, have the same fingerprint.
2. **a.** A latent print is a print that is not visible. It forms when sweat and oil are transferred from fingertips to the surface of an object.
   b. dusting, chemical reactions, and lighting
   c. Lighting may be used to reveal prints on a drinking glass, dusting may reveal prints on a doorknob, and fuming is used to reveal prints on an envelope.
3. **a.** Police want to eliminate some prints as evidence.
   b. The examiner compares ridge patterns, looks for details such as a split in a ridge, and then looks for small variations.
   c. With a computer database, an examiner has more data and the process is quicker.

Chapter 3

Reteach

L2 Ask students to make a flowchart showing the sequence of steps from the "discovery" of a fingerprint to finding a match. Tell them to assume that the fingerprint is latent.

Performance Assessment

L3 **ORAL PRESENTATION** Have students prepare a presentation on the techniques for dusting and lifting fingerprints.

L4 **WRITING** Ask students to compare eliminating fingerprints from evidence to the process a CSI uses to determine what objects to include in a crime scene sketch.

At-Home Activity: Family Fingerprints

Show the students how to use a soft pencil to make a dark area of graphite. Demonstrate how to make a fingerprint by rubbing a finger in the graphite and then rolling the finger from one side to the other on a piece of white paper. Caution students to make only one motion. They should not roll the finger back and forth on the paper.

Evidence From Blood

Reading Preview

OBJECTIVES

After this lesson, students will be able to

3.2.1 Describe the methods used to detect blood.
3.2.2 Explain how blood is classified.
3.2.3 Interpret patterns of bloodstains.

KEY TERMS

• hemoglobin • luminol • antibody

Target Reading Skill: Comparing and Contrasting

Organizing information in a table helps students find similarities and differences between objects.

SAMPLE ANSWERS

Students may include the following answers.

BLOOD TYPE	MARKER	CLUMPS WITH
Type A	A	Anti-A
Type B	B	Anti-B
Type AB	A, B	Anti-A, Anti-B
Type O	—	Neither

DIFFERENTIATED INSTRUCTION KEY

Use this key as you review the instructional strategies.

- **L1** For students with special needs
- **L2** For less proficient readers
- **L3** For all students
- **L4** For gifted and talented students
- **EL** For English language learners

Preteach

Build Background Knowledge: Blood

To prepare students for the concept of blood typing, explain that blood is a water-based mixture. Some substances are dissolved in the water. One example is glucose—a sugar the body uses for energy. Explain that there are cells suspended in the water. List the three types of cells—red blood cells, white blood cells, and platelets—on the board.

Ask students if they know what each cell does. Students may know that red blood cells carry oxygen to cells in the body and that white blood cells help protect the body from viruses and bacteria. Some students may know that platelets help form clots. Explain that red blood cells contain hemoglobin. This molecule carries oxygen to cells throughout the body. It can also be used to detect blood at a crime scene.

Set up a light microscope with a prepared slide of blood. Have students take turns viewing the slide under high power. Ask students to make a drawing of the cells that they observe.

Discover Activity — What Can Blood Drops Reveal? SE p. 80

SKILLS FOCUS Predicting

TIME 10 minutes

TEAM SIZE small group

MATERIALS large white sheet of paper, fake blood, metric ruler

TIPS Instruct the students to hold the dropper perpendicular to the floor.

EXPECTED OUTCOME Blood dropped from 20 cm forms a small round circle. Blood dropped from 100 cm forms a larger circle with ragged edges. There may also be a few small drops scattered around the large drop.

THINK IT OVER The drops would look like the drop that fell from the 100-cm height.

Instruct

Searching for Blood SE p. 81

Teach Key Concepts: Detecting Blood

L3 **FOCUS** State that, in a way, blood is similar to fingerprints. Sometimes the evidence is visible and sometimes it is hidden.

TEACH Discuss the story of the detective who used light to detect blood at a farmhouse in Pennsylvania. Then discuss using a chemical such as luminol to detect blood. **Q:** What happens when luminol is sprayed on a surface where there are traces of blood? **A:** The luminol emits a blue glow that lasts about 30 seconds. **Q:** What causes the luminol to glow? **A:** It reacts with the hemoglobin in red blood cells.

APPLY Ask students what would happen if the detective at the farmhouse sprayed luminol on the wood floor. (He would observe a blue glow.)

L2 Have students write a step-by-step description of how to do an initial test on a visible stain that looks like blood.

Teacher Demo: Testing for Blood

TIME 10 minutes

MATERIALS blood from tray used to package raw meat, 3% solution of hydrogen peroxide, eyedropper

SAFETY Wear gloves when handling blood, which may contain pathogens. Store the blood in the refrigerator in a labeled self-seal plastic bag. You can dispose of the bag in the trash.

FOCUS Tell students that you are going to demonstrate one of a series of reactions that takes place when luminol is used to detect blood.

TEACH Explain that a luminol solution contains substances other than luminol. Often, one of those substances is hydrogen peroxide. Add a few drops of hydrogen peroxide to the blood. Ask students to describe what they observe. (They should observe bubbles.) Explain that the bubbles contain oxygen, which is produced when hydrogen peroxide breaks down, or decomposes. Explain that the presence of hemoglobin speeds up this decomposition reaction.

FYI The iron in hemoglobin acts as a catalyst for a reaction that produces oxygen. (The oxygen reacts with the product of a reaction between luminol and hydroxide ions.) The amount of catalyst required is very small, which is why luminol can detect even tiny traces of blood.

Addressing Misconceptions: Blue Blood

FOCUS Some students think that blood is blue because of the apparent color of blood in veins near the surface of fair skin.

TEACH Explain to students that, despite appearances, all blood is red—bright red in arteries where the concentration of oxygen is high and a deeper red in veins where less oxygen is present.

FYI The actual explanation for why blood in veins appears blue differs from most explanations you will find online. The explanation is based on a theory of color perception proposed by Edwin Land—the inventor of the Polaroid camera. His theory states that humans perceive an object's color by comparing the light reflected by an object with the light reflected by adjacent objects—in this case the area of skin above a blood vessel and the areas of skin on either side.

Answers

FIGURE 5 hemoglobin

READING CHECKPOINT (SE p. 81) Hemoglobin is the molecule that carries oxygen to cells in the body.

Classifying Blood SE pp. 82–83

Teach Key Concepts: Blood Types

L3 **FOCUS** Explain that marker molecules on the surface of red blood cells are used to classify blood. Type A blood has A marker molecules. Type B blood has B marker molecules. Type AB blood has both types. Type O has neither.

TEACH Tell students that there are molecules called antibodies that can bind to other molecules. When the antibodies are for marker molecules in blood, the binding causes clumps to form in blood. **Q:** Which marker molecule would an Anti-A antibody bind to? **A:** an A molecule **Q:** Which marker molecule would an Anti-B antibody bind to? **A:** a B molecule

APPLY Use Figure 6 on SE p. 82. Have students describe what happens as each type of antibody is added to each type of blood.

L2 Ask students to imagine four cupcakes with red frosting. On one cupcake there are no candles. On a second cupcake there are blue candles. On a third there are white candles. On the fourth, there are both blue and white candles. Explain that the cupcakes represent red blood cells, the frosting represents the surface of a red blood cell, and the candles represent the A and B marker molecules.

EL Explain that the prefix *anti-* means "against" or "opposed to." Provide other examples of words that contain this prefix, such as *antiperspirant*, *antifreeze*, and *antisocial*.

L4 Tell students that the marker molecules on red blood cells are antigens. The term is short for *anti*body *gen*erating. Ask students to research how white blood cells destroy disease-causing organisms.

Chapter 3

Math Analyzing Data — Blood Type Distribution SE p. 83

MATH SKILL Calculating

FOCUS Ask students if they know what determines which blood type a person has. (Blood type is an inherited trait.) The distribution of blood types varies among populations. For example, the percentage of people with Type B blood is typically higher in Asia than in Western Europe. Explain that the word *frequency* can refer to how often something occurs, in this case a certain blood type in a population.

TEACH Remind students that the A and B markers are not the only markers on red blood cells. The Rh factor is found in some blood. Blood with this factor is Rh positive; blood without this factor is Rh negative. Explain that the percentages for receiving and donating blood are based on whole blood, which contains red blood cells.

NOTE When blood plasma is used instead of whole blood, the percentages for receiving and donating blood are reversed because plasma contains antibodies rather than antigens. People with AB positive blood become universal donors. People with O negative blood become universal recipients.

ANSWERS

1. O positive; AB negative
2. 16%
3. They can donate blood to a person with any blood type.
4. It decreases the number of likely donors; she may have antibodies for the Rh factor.

Skills Activity — Interpreting Data SE p. 82

TIME 10 minutes

TEAM SIZE individual

TIPS Tell students to use the chart in Figure 6 to help answer the questions.

ANSWERS

1. Type A or Type AB
2. Type A or Type O
3. Type B only
4. Type O only

Monitor Progress

L2 **ORAL PRESENTATION** Ask a student to identify the marker molecules, if any, that are in Type B blood. Ask another student to describe what happens if Type B blood is mixed with Anti-A antibodies. Ask what happens with Anti-B antibodies. Repeat this exercise for other blood types.

L3 **ORAL PRESENTATION** Ask students to explain how blood type is used to eliminate a suspect or narrow a list of suspects. Then ask why blood type can't be used to identify a suspect.

Answers

FIGURE 6 Type B and Type AB

READING CHECKPOINT (SE p. 83) Landsteiner was studying how to safely transfer blood from one person to another.

Go Online

FOR Links on blood type
VISIT www.SciLinks.org
WEB CODE dan-1032

Students can download a worksheet that will guide their review of Internet sources on blood types.

Bloodstain Patterns SE pp. 84–85

Teach Key Concepts: Bloodstains Tell a Story

L3 **FOCUS** Explain that investigators use the location, size, and shape of bloodstains to figure out what happened at a crime scene.

TEACH Use the results of the Discover Activity on SE p. 80 to discuss the effect of distance on the shape of bloodstains. Explain that when a surface is hard, the blood will bead up on the surface. When the surface is porous, the blood will spread out. Define *perpendicular* and have students draw a 90-degree angle. Ask students to predict what a stain would look like if blood hit a surface at an angle less then 90 degrees. Use a syringe, colored water, and paper to test the predictions.

APPLY Have students answer the questions in Figure 7 on SE p. 84. They will need to read about direction of travel to answer the third question.

L1 Have a peer describe the images in Figure 7 for visually impaired students.

L2 Make a recording of the paragraphs about direction of travel for students to listen to as they read.

EL Explain that an axis is an imaginary straight line that passes through the center of an object. On the board, draw a large version of one stain from the third panel of Figure 7. Draw a line through the center of the stain lengthwise and label it "long axis."

Build Inquiry: Force of Impact

MATERIALS dropper bottle with fake blood (or diluted red latex paint), plastic gloves, large sheets of construction paper or cardboard, metric ruler or tape, newspapers or plastic sheet

FOCUS Remind students that bloodstain patterns can reveal information about the force of a blow. Students can model what happens when blood travels at different velocities.

TEACH This activity can be done either by small groups or as a demonstration with student participation. Students should wear goggles, an apron, and gloves.

Place the paper or cardboard target on a chalk ledge or easel, or tape it to a wall. Put newspapers or a plastic sheet on the floor below the target. Have a student hold his left hand chest high with palm down and parallel to the floor about 20 cm from the target with the side of the hand toward the target. Have the student practice using his right hand to slap the back of the left hand with moderate force. The fingers of the right hand should be perpendicular to the target, and the hand should sweep forward and up like an airplane taking off. Demonstrate this motion, which will be used to propel the blood toward the target.

After the student has practiced, place a small (quarter-size) pool of fake blood on top of his left hand behind the knuckles. Have the student perform the slap. Label the target "medium-velocity impact at 90-degree angle." Remove the target and set it aside to dry.

Set up a new target. Repeat the activity, but have the student slap the back of his left hand with greater force. Label the second target "high-velocity impact at 90-degree angle."

Have students compare the number and size of the stains on the targets. The high-velocity impact should produce smaller stains. If time permits, have students propel blood toward fresh targets at different angles, producing elongated stains.

Answers

FIGURE 7 (1) The blood hit a surface at less than a 90-degree angle. (2) The drop that had ragged edges hit a porous surface. (3) The blood was traveling from left to right on impact because the tips of the blood spatter are pointing to the right.

Assess

Reviewing Key Concepts

1. a. Some chemicals produce light or change color in the presence of hemoglobin.
   b. Luminol can be used to search large areas quickly and can reveal traces of blood even after a crime scene is cleaned. But blood is not the only material that can cause luminol to glow.
2. a. A molecules and B molecules
   b. Type A and Type AB blood have A molecules, but only Type AB has B molecules.
   c. No, because many people have Type B blood.
3. a. *Sample answer:* They can use size, shape, number, and location.
   b. The blood probably fell a short distance at a 90-degree angle.
   c. An object could have been at that location during an attack.

Reteach

L2 Give a group of students 24 index cards. Have them label three cards A, three cards B, three cards O, three cards AB, six cards Anti-A and six Anti-B. Have students shuffle the blood type cards and place the pile text-side down. Have them do the same for the antibody cards. Ask students to take turns selecting a card from each pile and stating what would happen if the blood and the antibodies were mixed.

Performance Assessment

L3 **SKILLS CHECK** Make statements such as the following and ask students if the statements are true or false. Blood that falls a short distance onto a paper towel will leave a perfectly round stain. (false) When the narrow part of a bloodstain points left, the blood was traveling from right to left. (true) An empty space in the middle of blood spatter indicates that an object was in that location at the time of the attack. (true)

L2 **DRAWING** Have students make a drawing that shows the relationship between antibodies and the marker molecules on red blood cells.

In the Community: Blood Donors

Rather than have every student try to contact a Red Cross representative, invite a representative to visit your classroom. If you cannot arrange a visit, direct students to the American Red Cross Web site from which they can navigate to find information on donating blood. (They will also find some games related to blood types.)

Chapter Project

KEEP STUDENTS ON TRACK By now, students should have typed the blood found at the crime scene and used the results to identify the thief of the Missing Masterpiece.

Forensics & Life Science

Facial Reconstruction SE pp. 86–87

Background Forensic sculptors have been surprisingly successful at using a skull to rebuild the face of an unknown victim. Most sculptors use the technique described in the text, which is based on measurements of average depth of tissue by gender and ethnic group.

Sometimes a computer is used to make a reconstruction. The operator starts by using a laser to make a 3-D scan of the skull. A forensic anthropologist uses the skull and other evidence to infer the age, gender, and ethnicity of the victim. To add tissue to the skull, the operator uses a CAT scan of the head of a similar living person. A CAT scan records both hard and soft tissues. The availability of CAT scans has also allowed scientists to gather more reliable data on average tissue depth.

Teach Key Concepts

BUILDING A FACE

Tell students that a forensic anthropologist will study the skull and other bones found with the skull before an artist works with it. **Q:** What could an anthropologist infer from these observations? **A:** age, gender, and ethnicity **Q:** How will these inferences help a sculptor do a reconstruction? **A:** The sculptor would know which data to use to place the depth pegs. **Q:** At what other point in the process will the sculptor rely heavily on inferences? **A:** when deciding on final touches such as eye color

Go Online

FOR Links on animal symmetry
VISIT www.SciLinks.org
WEB CODE dan-1030

Download a worksheet for students.

Help Students Read

BUILD VOCABULARY

Explain that an organism has bilateral symmetry if a line can be drawn through the organism that divides it into halves that are mirror images. *Bilateral* means having "two sides."

Project an image of a face and ask students where to draw the line that divides the face into two halves. Note that there can be tiny differences between the two sides of a face that would be noticeable only if you could see the mirror image of one side imposed over the other side of the face. If you use "symmetry human face" to search for images online, you may find sites where a photographer had compared an image of a face to a similar image constructed from two left sides and two right sides.

Build Inquiry

MAKING A MODEL

MATERIALS image of skull, large Styrofoam™ egg, modeling clay, plastic knife

TIME 40 minutes

PREPARATION Plastic skulls would be ideal. Otherwise, you need a base for students to build on, such as a foam egg or a balloon (though the latter could prove fragile). You can use a search engine to find images of skulls.

TEACH This activity will give students some sense of the challenges of reconstructing a face. Note that a person's ears are roughly the same length as the nose, that the width of a nose is typically the same as the distance between the inner corners of the eyes, and that the mouth usually extends to the mid-point of each eye socket. When students are done, display the models. If you used images, have students try to match the models to the images.

You Be the Judge

1. The final touches are likely to be the least accurate because they are based mainly on inferences.
2. The length should be similar in most cases.
3. In general, an increase in overall weight adds greater depth to the flesh on a person's face.

Chapter 3

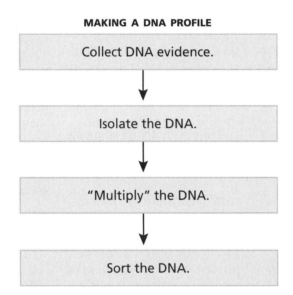

DNA Evidence

Reading Preview

OBJECTIVES

After this lesson, students will be able to

3.3.1 State the reason for DNA's value as a tool for forensic scientists.
3.3.2 Summarize the process for making a DNA profile.
3.3.3 Explain why DNA profiles are accepted as evidence.
3.3.4 Describe the uses of DNA profiles.

KEY TERMS

- DNA • protein • gene • DNA profile • replication
- probability • cold case • endangered species

Target Reading Skill: Sequencing

Remind students that a sequence is the order in which events occur. A flowchart can be used to help visualize the steps in a sequence.

SAMPLE ANSWERS

Students may include the following answers.

MAKING A DNA PROFILE

Collect DNA evidence.

↓

Isolate the DNA.

↓

"Multiply" the DNA.

↓

Sort the DNA.

DIFFERENTIATED INSTRUCTION KEY

Use this key as you review the instructional strategies.

L1 For students with special needs	L3 For all students	EL For English language learners
L2 For less proficient readers	L4 For gifted and talented students	

Preteach

Build Background Knowledge: Cell Structure

Distribute copies of, or project a diagram of, a typical animal cell. Explain that each type of structure in the cell has a specific function. **Q:** What is the function of the cell membrane? **A:** It controls what substances enter and leave the cell. **Q:** What takes place in the rod-shaped mitochondria? **A:** Energy is produced. **Q:** What molecules are produced in ribosomes? **A:** proteins **Q:** What is the function of the nucleus? **A:** The information that controls everything that takes place in a cell is stored in the nucleus. **Q:** How is this information stored? **A:** in a molecule called DNA

Discover Activity How Long Can You Make a Match? SE p. 88

SKILLS FOCUS Interpreting Data

TIME 15 minutes

TEAM SIZE individual

MATERIALS plastic snap cubes, three colors

TIPS This activity will give students a sense of why no two people, other than identical twins, have the exact same sequence of base pairs in their DNA. The triplets are not intended as a model of coding in DNA.

For visually impaired students, place containers with each color cube in a set order from left to right.

EXPECTED OUTCOME Students should notice that even with only three different colors, there are many possible combinations.

THINK IT OVER The number of matching strings decreases as the length of the string increases.

Instruct

DNA Molecules SE p. 89

Teach Key Concepts: DNA Is Unique

L3 **FOCUS** Ask students to think of some siblings they know who have the same biological parents. Ask for examples of physical traits that the siblings have in common. Then ask for examples of physical traits that vary among the siblings. Explain that every individual, except for identical twins, is different from his or her parents or siblings. This is because each person's DNA is unique and DNA determines a person's inherited traits.

TEACH Display false-color SEM or TEM photographs of different human cells. Check the Science Photo Library site. Identify the types of cells. Explain that the colors were added to highlight cell features. **Q:** What do all the cells have in common? **A:** a nucleus **Q:** If all the cells were from one individual, what could you infer? **A:** The DNA would be identical. **Q:** If all the cells came from different individuals, what could you infer? **A:** The DNA in each cell would be different.

APPLY Ask **Q:** Why is it possible to compare results of DNA tests done on cheek cells and hair? **A:** If the cells are from the same person, they will have identical DNA.

L1 Enlarge photographs you find online for visually impaired students.

Use Visuals: Figure 8

L3 **FOCUS** Hold up a long chain of paper clips. Explain that the chain could serve as a model for biological molecules such as carbohydrates and proteins. In both cases, smaller units join together to form a long, large molecule. In carbohydrates, the smaller units are sugars. In proteins, the units are amino acids.

TEACH Refer students to Figure 8 on SE p. 89. Point out that DNA is also made up of smaller units. The units in each strand of DNA have three parts—a sugar, a phosphate group, and a nitrogen base. The strands are held together by weak chemical bonds between a pair of bases. **Q:** What are the names of the four nitrogen bases in a DNA molecule? **A:** adenine, cytosine, guanine, and thymine **Q:** How do the bases pair up? **A:** adenine with thymine; guanine with cytosine

Explain that the order of the bases along a strand of DNA is a code. Cells use this code to produce proteins. **Q:** What is the name for a section of DNA that contains information to make one protein? **A:** a gene

L1 Use a 3-D model of DNA to allow visually impaired students to feel the structure of DNA.

L4 Ask students to prepare an oral presentation about how the sequence of nitrogen bases determines which protein is produced. Ask students to focus on the relationship between triplets in the DNA sequence and amino acids.

Build Inquiry: Make a Model of DNA

TIME 20 minutes

MATERIALS licorice, four colors of small gumdrops, toothpicks

CAUTION Remind students not to eat the supplies or the finished models.

TEACH Have students work in pairs. Give each pair two strands of licorice and a sufficient supply of gumdrops and toothpicks. Tell students which color gumdrop represents each nitrogen base. Remind students that A and T always bond as do C and G. Suggest that students make a sketch of the section of DNA that they want to construct before they begin.

Use toothpicks with two pointed ends so students can construct the base pairs and then use the ends to connect the base pairs to the licorice strands. Once all the toothpicks are in place, students should gently twist the licorice strands to form the double helix structure.

Monitor Progress

L2 **SKILLS CHECK** Give students a diagram showing a sequence of bases such as -A-T-T-A-C-C-A-G-G- and have students write down the sequence for the second strand.

Answers

FIGURE 8 adenine; cytosine

READING CHECKPOINT (SE p. 89) Proteins control the chemical reactions that take place in cells.

Making a DNA Profile SE pp. 90–91

Teach Key Concepts: DNA Testing

L3 **FOCUS** Explain that the process for testing DNA begins when a biological sample is collected from a crime scene or from a suspect. It ends when fragments of DNA are sorted to form a distinctive pattern. In between, the DNA must be removed from the biological sample. Sometimes the amount of DNA must be increased before the DNA can be sorted.

TEACH Explain that a biological sample must not be contaminated with cells from another person at any point in the process. Otherwise, the DNA profile will not be accurate. Use Figure 9 on SE p. 90 to discuss isolating DNA from a sample. The specific process will vary, but the approach described in the text is representative.

Tell students that the amount of DNA isolated from a biological sample may be too small to analyze. Explain that scientists use DNA's ability to make copies of itself to increase the amount of DNA. The scientist copies selected segments of DNA. **Q:** What does the scientist have after the DNA is "multiplied"? **A:** a mass of DNA fragments **Q:** What property is used to sort the fragments? **A:** the length of the fragments

APPLY Use Figure 10 on SE p. 91 to walk students through the process of DNA replication. **Q:** What must happen before the strands unwind? **A:** The bonds between the base pairs must break. **Q:** As the molecule begins to unwind, what happens to the bases on the single strands? **A:** Nitrogen bases in the nucleus bond to bases on the strands. **Q:** What rule guides how bases are added? **A:** A bonds with T; C bonds with G.

L1 Draw two 3-cm by 9-cm rectangles on a sheet of paper. About two thirds of the way along one rectangle, draw a pointed notch like the one on base pair C and G in Figure 8. Draw a circular notch on the second rectangle to represent the bond between A and T. Make copies of the sheet for students. Have them color and label the halves of each rectangle. Then have them cut apart the "bases" at the notches. Ask them to try to pair up C and A or G and T. Students should realize that the bases only fit together when A is paired with T and C is paired with G.

L4 Refer students to Figure 13 on SE p. 93. Explain that sometimes when DNA is sorted, the result is a graph. Have students compare the graph with the one on SE p. 60. Then ask them what DNA sorting and gas chromatography have in common. (In each case a mixture is sorted based on the size of the particles in the mixture.)

Skills Activity — Drawing Conclusions SE p. 90

TIME 10 minutes

TEAM SIZE pair

MATERIALS partial bar code and sheet of complete bar codes

L3 **TIPS** Explain that a bar code represents the DNA profile. Each bar code is specific for one product, just as each DNA profile is specific for one individual.

EXPECTED OUTCOME Students should be able to make a match by comparing the thicknesses of the lines on the bar code and the distances between lines.

L1 If you have access to a Braille labeler, make labels with different combinations of 12 numbers. Make one partial label that matches a portion of one complete label.

Chapter 3

Teacher Demo: Isolating DNA

TIME 15 minutes

MATERIALS strawberry, freezer bag, small graduated cylinder, liquid detergent, medium test tube, test tube rack, funnel, filter paper, chilled ethanol, stirring rod

FOCUS Explain that you are going to remove DNA from the cells in a strawberry.

TEACH Place a strawberry in the freezer bag and squeeze the bag to break apart the strawberry. Add 10 mL of detergent to the bag and squeeze the bag for a minute. Explain that the detergent breaks down the cell walls and the membrane that surrounds the nucleus in each cell. The DNA dissolves in the detergent.

Place a test tube in a test tube rack and place a filter paper cone in a funnel. Pour the liquid from the freezer bag through the funnel into the test tube until the test tube is about one-eighth full. Use the stirring rod to slowly pour the chilled ethanol down the side of the test tube. Add ethanol until the test tube is about one-half full. Then place the end of the stirring rod at the point where the two layers meet and gently twirl the rod. The DNA will precipitate out of solution as a sticky white solid.

Help Students Read: Building Vocabulary

L2 Explain that a profile is an outline or a summary. It could be a drawing of the side view of a person's face or of the layers in soil or bedrock. A profile can also be a brief written summary about a person. The profiles FBI agents write generally focus on a criminal's motivations, personality, and patterns of behavior. A DNA profile is a description, too. It is a visual description of selected segments of a person's DNA.

EL Ask students if they have visited a museum or a park that has a copy of a famous object. Examples are the copy of the Parthenon in Centennial Park in Nashville, Tennessee, and the copy of Henry Hudson's ship *Half Moon* in Verplanck, New York. Tell students that these copies are called *replicas.* The act or process of copying is called *replication.*

Monitor Progress

L3 **ORAL PRESENTATION** Play a version of *Jeopardy!* with the class where the category is "Making a DNA Profile." The answer "the base that bonds with adenine," for example, should elicit the question "What is thymine?"

Answers

FIGURE 9 to avoid contamination of the sample and to protect the investigator

READING CHECKPOINT (SE p. 91) Replication is the process by which a DNA molecule makes a copy of itself.

Probability SE p. 92

Teach Key Concepts: The Number of Possibiities

L3 **FOCUS** Explain that DNA testing is a powerful tool because the probability of two people having the same DNA profile is extremely low.

TEACH Remind students that probability is the measure of the chance that an event will happen. Hold up a quarter. **Q:** When a coin is tossed, what is the probability that the coin will land heads up? **A:** 1 in 2 or 50%

Hold up a six-sided die. **Q:** What is the probability that this die lands with the side numbered 5 facing up? **A:** 1 in 6 or 16.7%

Fan out a pack of cards. **Q:** What is the probability that a person will select the ten of diamonds from this pack? **A:** 1 in 52 or 1.9% **Q:** Why did the odds decrease from the coin to the die to the pack of cards? **A:** The number of possibilities increased.

APPLY Review the results of the Discover Activity. Explain that the probability of a match decreased because the number of possible sequences increased.

L2 Review how to convert a fraction to a percent. Explain that probability is a ratio of an outcome to the total number of possible outcomes.

Teach the Big Idea

Use Visuals: Figure 12

L3 **FOCUS** Read aloud the Big Idea question for the chapter: What are some traits that scientists can use to identify an individual? Explain that scientists can use variation in certain segments of non-coding DNA to identify an individual. One of the segments forensic scientists use is TH01.

TEACH Have students write down the sequence of bases from left to right in the top strand in the first segment of Figure 12. **Q:** What base sequence repeats? **A:** A-A-T-G **Q:** How many times does this sequence repeat in the first segment? **A:** 6 **Q:** In the second segment? **A:** 8

Explain that in segment TH01, A-A-T-G can repeat from 5 to 11 times. A person can inherit the same variation from each parent or a different variation from each parent. Scientists can tell from a DNA profile which variations a person inherited because a fragment with fewer repeats will travel faster than a fragment with a greater number of repeats.

In every one of the other 12 segments that forensic scientists use to make DNA profiles the number of repeats of a particular base sequence can vary. The chance that two people have the exact same set of variations in all 13 segments is 1 in 500 trillion.

L4 The Math Practice on SE p. 95 is challenging. You may want to have your gifted students try solving it on their own before you show students how to begin to solve the problem.

Answers

FIGURE 12 six; eight

READING CHECKPOINT (SE p. 92) A-A-T-G

Chapter 3

Go Online

FOR Links on DNA fingerprinting
VISIT www.SciLinks.org
WEB CODE dan-1033

Students can download a worksheet that will guide their review of Internet sources on DNA fingerprinting.

Uses of DNA Profiles SE pp. 93–95

Teach Key Concepts: Wide Range of Uses for DNA

L3 **FOCUS** Explain that since DNA testing became possible, the uses of DNA profiles have multiplied.

TEACH Ask the following questions. **Q:** What is a cold case? **A:** an old, unsolved case **Q:** Can DNA be used to solve every cold case? Why or why not? **A:** DNA can be used only when the saved evidence includes a biological sample from the offender. **Q:** What is CODIS? **A:** a database of DNA profiles **Q:** How is CODIS used to solve cold cases? **A:** A profile made from crime scene evidence is compared with profiles of known offenders.

WARNING Be cautious about asking students to research specific examples of the use of DNA to solve cold cases or to free prisoners. The story of Ryan Matthews that is used in the textbook is not typical. Many cases involve rapes and the biological sample used to make a profile is semen.

APPLY Tell students about Cheddar Man—a 9,000-year-old skeleton found in a cave in Cheddar, England, in 1903. In the 1990s, scientists wanted to know whether any current Cheddar residents were related to Cheddar Man. Ask students to predict what the scientists did to find out. After students offer their predictions, tell them that scientists extracted non-nuclear DNA from Cheddar Man's jaw. They collected cheek cells from 20 current residents of Cheddar. They used the samples to make DNA profiles. When the profiles were compared, scientists concluded that one of the current residents and the Cheddar Man shared a common ancestor.

EL Help students find a list of endangered or threatened species in their countries of origin. Ask students to pick a species and do some research on why the species is endangered and what is being done to protect it.

L4 Ask students to research how DNA is being used to study migration patterns of human populations and the ancestry of individuals.

Answers

FIGURE 13 Suspect 2, because the locations of the peaks on the suspect's profile match the locations on the profile from the crime scene sample

FIGURE 14 *Sample answer:* Either the DNA was damaged when the bodies decayed or bone cells do not have a nucleus.

READING CHECKPOINT (SE p. 94) His DNA profile did not match the profile made from DNA found on a ski mask left at the crime scene.

Assess

Reviewing Key Concepts

1. a. Two long strands of DNA are coiled around each other. Weak chemical bonds between pairs of nitrogen bases connect the strands.
   b. *Sample answer:* DNA is divided into sections. In some sections, called genes, the order of the bases is a code for producing a specific protein.
   c. No, because a child's DNA is a combination of DNA inherited from the parents and, except for identical twins, no two people have the same nuclear DNA.

2. a. In non-coding DNA, there is variation in the number of times a base sequence is repeated.
   b. Scientists collect a sample that contains DNA, isolate the DNA, multiply it, and then sort it.
   c. length; The shortest fragments will travel most quickly.

3. a. With 13 segments there is a much greater probability that no two people would have the same profile.
   b. Scientists use DNA profiles to connect a suspect to a crime, solve cold cases, free the innocent, identify human remains, and protect endangered species.
   c. They can compare the profile with one made from crime scene evidence or with profiles stored in a database.

Reteach

L2 Distribute the following paragraph and ask students to fill in the blanks. Except for identical twins, no two people have DNA with the exact same sequence of ______. A section of DNA called a ______ controls the production of a specific protein. To make a DNA profile, scientists must ______, ______, ______, and ______ DNA. As the number of DNA segments tested ______, the probability of two people having the same DNA profile decreases. DNA profiles of known offenders are stored in an FBI database called ______.

Performance Assessment

L3 **SKILLS CHECK** Supply snap cubes in four colors. Indicate which base each color represents. Give each student an index card on which you have written a sequence of bases. Have students construct the segment of DNA that contains this sequence.

L2 **DRAWING** Have students design a flowchart to show the sequence involved in making a DNA profile. Offer points for creativity.

Math Practice

MATH SKILL: Probability

4. There are 28 possible combinations: 7 + 6 + 5 + 4 + 3 + 2 + 1; 1 divided by 28 equals 3.6%. Suggest that students make a grid with the numbers 1 to 7 across the top and 1 to 7 down the side. Have them fill in the seven boxes in the first row with the combinations 1 + 1, 1 + 2, and so on. Have them proceed down the rows, filling in only those combinations that have not already been used. Remind students that 1 + 6 is the same as 6 + 1.

Handwriting and Voice Identification

Reading Preview

OBJECTIVES

After this lesson, students will be able to

3.4.1 Identify clues used to compare writing samples.
3.4.2 Describe the methods analysts use to compare voice samples.

KEY TERMS

- voiceprint

Target Reading Skill: Identifying Main Ideas

Students need to be able to identify details that support the main idea of a paragraph or section. This ability will help students with their reading comprehension and provide a model for their own writing.

SAMPLE ANSWERS

Students may include the following answers.

MAIN IDEA

Handwriting experts look at the style of the handwriting and the content.

- They look at the shape, slant, and size of letters.
- They look at word choices, spelling, and punctuation.
- They look to see if a document has been altered.

DIFFERENTIATED INSTRUCTION KEY

Use this key as you review the instructional strategies.

- **L1** For students with special needs
- **L2** For less proficient readers
- **L3** For all students
- **L4** For gifted and talented students
- **EL** For English language learners

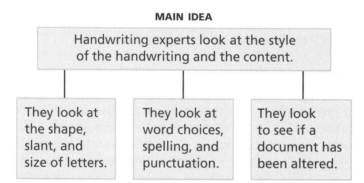

Preteach

Build Background Information: Content Clues

Ask a librarian to help you select two age-appropriate authors who write in the same genre but have noticeably different styles. Read a brief passage by each author and ask students to decide whether the passages were written by the same author or different authors. Ask students what clues they used to decide. Don't pick well-known authors so students must use clues in the writing to answer the question.

Discover Activity — Can Handwriting Identify a Person? SE p. 96

SKILLS FOCUS Inferring

TIME 15 minutes

TEAM SIZE individual

MATERIALS multiple signatures on a sheet of paper, hand lens

TIPS With a hand lens, it will be easier for students to compare details in the signatures.

EXPECTED OUTCOME There will probably be more variation in details among signatures than within a single signature.

THINK IT OVER Students may disagree about whether a handwriting sample can be used to identify a suspect. Accept any answer that is reasonable.

Instruct

Handwriting Identification SE pp. 97–98

Teach Key Concepts: Handwriting Styles

L3 **FOCUS** Point out that handwriting is distinctive and can be used to connect a suspect to a crime.

TEACH Print your name on the board and write your signature. Explain that even in school districts where students learn to print, students are often taught to write a cursive signature. **Q:** What kinds of documents require a signature? **A:** *Sample answer:* a check, driver's license, a tax return, a lease **Q:** Why is a cursive signature preferred to a printed name on such documents? **A:** *Sample answer:* because it is more difficult to copy (forge) a cursive signature

APPLY Have at least six volunteers write their signatures on the board. As a class, analyze the signatures by looking for similarities and differences.

L2 Discuss similarities between the process of comparing signatures and the process of comparing fingerprints.

EL Pose the following questions. Does a person's handwriting change when the person writes in two different languages that share a similar alphabet? When a person writes in two different languages that have distinctly different alphabets? Depending on the backgrounds of your students, you may be able to gather data to answer one or both of these questions. Ask students to write a short sentence on the board in their native language and the translation of the sentence in English.

Addressing Misconceptions: Is Handwriting Reliable?

L3 **FOCUS** Handwriting experts argue that no two individuals share the same handwriting. Critics argue that there is no scientific basis for this claim.

TEACH Tell students that handwriting experts rate the possibility of a match on a nine-point scale from 1 equaling identification to 9 equaling elimination. Some factors increase the reliability of the conclusions, such as a larger number of samples or samples that contain the same words.

L4 Ask students to research the use of handwriting samples in the Bruno Hauptmann trial. If they do, they will discover that investigators did things at the time that would not be accepted practice today. For example, investigators showed Bruno the ransom notes and asked him to make handwritten copies of the content.

Answers

FIGURE 16 *Sample answer:* In both samples, the writing slants up. The letters in RT's sample are larger and they are connected within words.

READING CHECKPOINT (SE p. 98) Experts look for letters the writer tends to leave out.

Voice Identification SE pp. 98–99

Teach Key Concepts: Voice Recognition Provides Clues

L3 **FOCUS** Ask students if they have seen a TV show or movie in which agents are sitting in a van listening to a conversation that is taking place in a nearby building. Law enforcement agencies usually need to get permission from a court to listen to private conversations.

TEACH Tell students that the people who listen to recorded conversations quickly learn to recognize who is speaking. Make a list on the board of clues a listener may use to recognize a speaker—low or high pitch, fast or slow pace, soft or loud, pronunciation (especially variations in vowel sounds), word choice, whether the pitch rises or falls at the end of a sentence, and so on.

APPLY Suppose an agent listening to a tape hears something that the agent thinks could be used as evidence in court. **Q:** What could the agent do to prove that the person speaking on the tape is the suspect? **A:** The agent could make a voiceprint of the statement and compare it to a voiceprint made from a recorded interview with the suspect.

L1 Play a recording of an audio book. Have hearing-impaired students hold a balloon in front of their face and feel the balloon vibrate in response to the sound waves produced by the voice.

Answers

FIGURE 18 *Sample answer:* The gap represents a pause between words.

Skills Activity Observing SE p. 98

TIME 10 minutes

TEAM SIZE class

MATERIALS recording of voices

TIPS Ask one or more students to try to disguise their voices.

EXPECTED OUTCOME The students will likely recognize some or all of the voices. They may suggest that pitch, loudness, pace, accent, and choice of words helped them identify the speakers.

Assess

Reviewing Key Concepts

1. a. shapes, slant, and relative size
   b. word choice, spelling, and punctuation
   c. *Sample answer:* the grocery list because the suspect might have tried to disguise his writing style in the test sample
2. a. They can use a machine to graph the sounds or listen to recordings.
   b. The voiceprint can measure pitch and loudness.
   c. breathing patterns, pronunciations, phrasing, or word usage

Reteach

L2 Compare the process of analyzing a voiceprint with handwriting analysis.

Performance Assessment

Divide students into small groups. Have each student copy two passages you have written on the board onto two separate index cards. Have groups mix up their cards and exchange their stack with another group. The groups should then pair up the cards in their stack by writer.

Writing in Science

WRITING MODE: Advertisement

SCORING RUBRIC

4	Exceeds criteria; is well-written, creative, and has detailed descriptions of voice qualities
3	Meets criteria; describes relevant voice qualities
2	Does not describe relevant voice qualities
1	Is incomplete or inaccurate

Skills Lab Measuring Writing SE p. 100

KEY CONCEPT
Handwriting experts look at the style of the handwriting.

SKILLS OBJECTIVE
After this lab, students will be able to
- make quantitative measurements of handwriting samples
- calculate the mean and describe the range of data

CLASS TIME 45 minutes

TEAM SIZE individual

See pp. 95–98 in the Student Handbook, ATE for additional information.

Chapter 3

Chapter Review

Study Guide SE p. 101

Apply the Big Idea

Connect to Key Concepts

Reinforce the Big Idea by connecting it to important Key Concepts. For example, ask: "Why do scientists analyze more than one sequence of DNA when they make a DNA profile? (As the number of segments tested increases, the probability of two people having the same DNA profile decreases.)

Variation in Traits

Remind students that a trait must show variation in order to be useful for identifying a suspect. Have students discuss the usefulness of blood types as compared to DNA for identifying a suspect. Ask them to compare the amount of variation possible with blood types to the amount of variation possible with DNA.

Review and Assessment SE pp. 102–103

Organizing Information

a. visible or plastic
b. visible or plastic
c. dusting
d. chemical reactions

Reviewing Key Terms

1. c 2. a 3. b 4. d
5. False; plastic print
6. True 7. True
8. False; cold case
9. False; voiceprint

Writing in Science

WRITING MODE: News Report

SCORING RUBRIC

4	Exceeds criteria; shows an excellent understanding of the methods used for detecting blood
3	Meets criteria; includes four relevant questions
2	Does not meet criteria; includes three or fewer questions
1	Does not include any relevant questions

Checking Concepts

10. The patterns are classified as loops, whorls, and arches.
11. Visible prints are the marks left by a colored substance on a person's fingertips; plastic prints are impressions made in soft materials; latent prints are made by sweat or oils on skin.
12. They first eliminate the prints of non-suspects. Then they compare the remaining prints with those of a suspect or with prints in a database.
13. An antibody is a molecule that binds to a specific marker molecule. If that marker molecule is in a sample of blood and the antibody is added, the blood will clump.
14. Investigators collect evidence containing DNA. Then they isolate, multiply, and sort the DNA.
15. Bonds between the base pairs break and the strands separate. The molecule unwinds. Unattached bases bond to the bases on the strands according to the A + T and C + G rule. As the bases are added, the molecule rewinds.

16. A DNA database includes DNA profiles of offenders who were convicted of certain violent crimes, profiles of missing persons, and profiles from forensic evidence.
17. *Sample answer:* style of writing, such as size and shape of letters; and content, such as word choice
18. *Sample answer:* They can identify properties such as pitch and loudness and look for distinctive patterns on the graph.

Thinking Critically

19. No. Fingerprints are more useful because no two individuals have the same fingerprints, but many people have the same blood type.
20. The chemical reacts with chemicals in the sweat absorbed by the surface.
21. *Sample answer:* Nuclear DNA is a combination of DNA from a mother and a father. The DNA found outside the nucleus is inherited only from the mother.
22. The scientist could make a DNA profile from a sample of the whale meat and compare it to a known profile from the protected species.
23. *Sample answer:* The expert might be looking at signatures.

Math Practice

24. 50%, 17%

Applying Skills

25. A = 30%, C = 20%, G = 20%, T = 30%
26. There is the same percentage of A and T. There is the same percentage of C and G.
27. In a DNA molecule, A always pairs with T, and C always pairs with G.
28. 25%

Chapter Project

PERFORMANCE ASSESSMENT The presentations should show an understanding of blood types and how blood typing can be used to eliminate suspects.

Chapter 4

Bringing Evidence to Court

Chapter at a Glance SE pp. 104–131

		Resources
Project	Conducting a Trial	• Chapter Project Worksheet
Lesson 1	**From Arrest to Trial** 4.1.1 Explain how a person's rights are protected before, during, and after an arrest. 4.1.2 Classify crimes as felonies or misdemeanors. 4.1.3 Summarize what typically happens between an arrest and a trial.	• Vocabulary Worksheet • Reading and Note Taking Guide 4-1 • Video Viewing Guide 4 • Video: Bill of Rights
Lesson 2	**Presenting Evidence in a Trial** 4.2.1 Compare the assigned roles of a judge, an impartial jury, and the lawyers at a criminal trial. 4.2.2 Identify ways that lawyers use exhibits in court. 4.2.3 Explain how lawyers use witnesses to present evidence.	• Reading and Note Taking Guide 4-2 • Skills Lab Worksheet • Laboratory Investigation 11: Expert Opinions • Video: Trial by Jury
	Forensics & Technology Modeling a Crime Scene	• SciLinks: lasers • Video: Virtual Crime Scenes
Lesson 3	**The Final Stages of a Trial** 4.3.1 Describe the process a jury uses to reach a verdict. 4.3.2 State what happens when a person is found guilty.	• Reading and Note Taking Guide 4-3
Review and Assessment		• Chapter 4 Test • Unit Test

Chapter Activities Planner

Activity/Time	Inquiry	Team Size/Materials	Skills
Chapter Project 2 periods	Guided	Team Size: small group poster board, scissors, markers, fact sheets	making models, inferring, drawing conclusions
Lesson 1			
Discover Activity 15 minutes	Guided	Team Size: pair	developing hypotheses
Skills Activity 10 minutes	Guided	Team Size: individual	making judgments
Lesson 2			
Discover Activity 10 minutes	Open-ended	Team Size: pair	making judgments
Skills Activity 10 minutes	Guided	Team Size: individual	calculating
Skills Activity 10 minutes	Guided	Team Size: individual	posing questions
At-Home Activity 45 minutes	Open-ended	Team Size: small group printed map of community, phone directory	making models
Skills Lab 45 minutes	Guided	Team Size: small group metric ruler, 2 pieces of graph paper, 2 pieces of cardboard, transparent tape	making models, measuring, calculating
Lesson 3			
Discover Activity 10 minutes	Guided	Team Size: pair	posing questions

Chapter 4

Bringing Evidence to Court

From the Author

In Chapter 4, the focus shifts from the crime lab to the courtroom. Students can gain a new perspective on topics that were introduced in earlier chapters. For example, they will learn that a lawyer for the defense may ask to exclude evidence because a search was not legal or because a chain of custody was not maintained. Students will also see that the role of forensic scientists extends beyond the laboratory. Forensic scientists often appear in court as expert witnesses.

Chapter 4 provides a valuable lesson on rights and responsibilities in a democracy. People who are accused of crimes have rights, including the right to a jury trial. Adult citizens have the responsibility to serve on juries.

You might want to ask a social studies colleague to collaborate with you on this chapter. Together, you can help students identify ways in which science and social studies are similar. In both disciplines, for example, it is important to distinguish fact from opinion.

Background

FEDERAL AND STATE COURTS The U.S. Constitution gives certain powers to the federal government. It reserves all other powers for the states. Both levels of government need courts to hear cases related to the laws their legislatures enact. In the federal court system, there are 94 U.S. District Courts, 13 U.S. Circuit Courts of Appeals, and the U.S. Supreme Court. There are also specialized courts that deal with matters such as taxes and trade.

Most states have three levels of courts. Cases usually begin in a trial court. Some trial courts have limited jurisdiction—conflicts within families, small claims, and so on. In these courts, a judge usually presides without a jury. The main state trial courts hear cases that fall outside the jurisdiction of the specialized courts. There is usually a judge and a jury. The judge decides issues of law; the jury decides issues of fact.

In many states, there is a level of courts between the trial courts and the highest court in the state. In these appellate courts, a panel of two or three judges hears appeals of verdicts from the trial court. In most states, the highest court is called a supreme court. Some cases begin in the supreme court, for example, cases related to elections.

CRIMINAL VS. CIVIL LAW In a criminal case, a prosecutor working for a state or for the federal government is the accuser. The prosecution must prove its case against the defendant "beyond a reasonable doubt." If a defendant is found guilty, he or she may be imprisoned. Only the defense can appeal the verdict in a criminal case.

A civil case is a dispute between individuals or between individuals and organizations, including businesses and governments. The burden of proof in a civil case is sometimes described as "more likely than not." Both parties in a civil case may be found to be partially at fault. A person who is found at fault does not serve time in jail or in prison. Either party in a civil case can appeal the verdict.

Focus on the Big Idea

Use the Big Idea question as a way to activate prior knowledge.

PRESENT THE IDEA Read aloud the Big Idea question. Explain that a trial is used to determine whether the person being accused of a crime is guilty. Tell students that sometimes a person who is guilty goes free and sometimes a person who is innocent is convicted. For most people, the conviction of a person who is innocent is more troubling than the failure to convict a person who is guilty. English judge William Blackstone (1723–1780) said, "Better that ten guilty persons escape than that one innocent suffer." One way to support this principle of justice is to make sure that those who are accused of crimes have a fair trial.

DISCUSSION QUESTIONS Then ask the following questions. **Q:** When you say something is "not fair," what do you mean? **A:** *Sample answers:* "Not fair" means not following the rules or cheating. "Not fair" means one person gets treated differently than another. **Q:** What do you think could make a trial "not fair"? **A:** Accept any reasonable answers and tell students that they should keep this question in mind as they study Chapter 4.

FOLLOW UP See the Teach the Big Idea instruction strategy on TG p. 116.

Forensic Science Videos Video Viewing Guide 4

Discovery EDUCATION

VIDEO Bill of Rights

TIME 3:48 minutes

DESCRIPTION This video provides historical context for the Bill of Rights and summarizes the rights protected by each amendment.

TEACHING TIPS You might want to draw a timeline on the board with dates for key events from the Declaration of Independence to the Bill of Rights.

VIDEO Trial by Jury

TIME 4:17 minutes

DESCRIPTION This video explains the role of a jury in a trial and compares that role to the roles of the prosecution, defense, and judge.

TEACHING TIPS You can use this video to introduce the topic or to provide support for your less proficient readers.

VIDEO Virtual Crime Scenes

TIME 4:57 minutes

DESCRIPTION This video compares the traditional method for making a diagram of a crime scene to the method that employs a laser scanner to generate a 3-D visual. The emphasis is on the advantages of using a laser scanner.

TEACHING TIPS You can use this video to introduce the Forensics & Technology feature on modeling a crime scene.

Chapter 4 Project SE p. 105

Conducting a Trial

SKILLS OBJECTIVES
After this activity, students will be able to
- prepare visual displays to summarize test results
- develop a strategy for communicating their hypothesis of a crime
- demonstrate appropriate courtroom procedures while presenting their case

TEACHING TIP You probably won't have time for every team to present its case. You may want to select only one team to act as prosecutors. If so, students from other teams can play the judge, the court clerk, and defense lawyers. The remaining students can be part of an expanded jury.

Plan the Case

CLASS TIME 45 minutes

TEAM SIZE 5–6 students

MATERIALS Have plenty of poster board and markers available for student posters.

BEGIN THE PROJECT Tell students that they will use the results of previous chapter projects to prove to a jury that the defendant is guilty.

TEACHING TIPS Explain to students that the teams that do the best job preparing their cases are most likely to be selected to present their case in the mock trial.

Students can use the scale models they made in the Chapter 4 Skills Lab. Students may also have prepared posters and other exhibits as part of the performance assessment for the other chapter projects.

Make sure the teams fill out the data tables in Part 1. These tables provide a way to organize information as students plan the presentation of their case.

Present the Case

PREP TIME 30 minutes

CLASS TIME 45 minutes

TEAM SIZE class

MATERIALS courtroom fact sheets

ADVANCE PREPARATION At www.phschool.com, enter Web Code daf-1000 to access PDF files of the courtroom fact sheets. Print out the pages and have them ready to distribute to students according to their assigned roles.

TEACHING TIPS The fact sheets provide general guidelines for each trial participant. Have the lawyers take turns questioning witnesses. Remind students on the defense team that they must make sure the prosecution follows the rules. They should try to cast doubt on the prosecution's case. For example, they can challenge the methods used or the results of a team's analysis of evidence. They can offer alternative explanations.

Ask students who are assigned to the jury to elect a foreperson. Allow enough time for the jury deliberation so students can gain firsthand experience of the process.

EXPECTED OUTCOME Evaluate students on the process, not on the verdict. For example, the prosecution should present witnesses in a logical order. The defense should object to leading questions. The judge should give appropriate instructions to the jury. Members of the jury should focus on the evidence during their deliberation.

Alternative Crime Scene

The fact sheets are independent of the crime scenario. Your class should be able to use the instructions and fact sheets with any scenario that you create.

Lesson 4-1 SE pp. 106–112

From Arrest to Trial

Reading Preview

OBJECTIVES

After this lesson, students will be able to

4.1.1 Explain how a person's rights are protected before, during, and after an arrest.

4.1.2 Classify crimes as felonies or misdemeanors.

4.1.3 Summarize what typically happens between an arrest and a trial.

KEY TERMS

- Bill of Rights
- jury
- bail
- felony
- misdemeanor
- probable cause
- defendant
- judge
- prosecutor
- public defender
- plea bargain

Target Reading Skill: Building Vocabulary

Explain that knowing the definitions of Key Terms helps students understand what they read. As students read the lesson, encourage them to make flash cards. Have them write a Key Term on one side of an index card and a definition of the term in their own words on the other side.

SAMPLE ANSWERS

Student answers should contain the most important feature or function of each term. For example, the definition of *probable cause* should stress that the belief needs to be reasonable.

DIFFERENTIATED INSTRUCTION KEY

Use this key as you review the instructional strategies.

L1 For students with special needs	L3 For all students
L2 For less proficient readers	L4 For gifted and talented students
EL For English language learners	

Preteach

Build Background Knowledge: Branches of Government

L3 Explain that government at both the state and federal level is organized into the executive branch, the legislative branch, and the judicial branch. This arrangement is intended to keep any one branch from having too much power. The legislative branch makes the laws, the executive branch enforces the laws, and the judicial branch interprets and applies the laws. **Q:** For which branch of government do the police work, and why? **A:** The police are part of the executive branch because they help enforce laws. (A state's crime lab is also part of the executive branch.)

L1 Explain that the people who make the laws and the head of the executive branch are elected officials.

L4 Have students use "state government" as a search term to find a directory of official state Web sites. Have students bookmark your state's site and refer to it as they study Chapter 4.

Discover Activity — When Is a Suspect Guilty? SE p. 106

SKILLS FOCUS Developing Hypotheses

TIME 15 minutes

TEAM SIZE pair

TIPS The goal of this activity is to introduce the concept "presumed innocent until proven guilty." You might want to display newspaper clippings about crimes that include the words *alleged* or *allegedly*.

EXPECTED OUTCOME Students should realize that an arrest is only the first step in a process that will determine whether or not a person is guilty.

THINK IT OVER Some students may argue that Clara might be innocent. Other students may argue that, even if Clara did take the books, her guilt must be proven in a court of law.

Instruct

The Bill of Rights SE pp. 107–108

Teach Key Concepts: Protection of Individual Rights

L3 **FOCUS** Explain that many delegates to the Constitutional Convention were worried about a federal government with too much power. So they assigned a limited set of powers to the federal government and left all other matters to the states. They also distributed the power of the government across three separate branches. Finally, they added amendments to the U.S. Constitution to protect the rights of individuals.

TEACH Make copies of the Bill of Rights for students. (The U.S. National Archives and Records Administration Web site has a printable version.) For most students, the language used in the Bill of Rights will be challenging. Rewrite the first amendment on the board, using simpler words and constructions. Use historic events (such as the trial of John Peter Zenger in 1735) or current events (such as a protest rally or march) as examples of rights protected by the first amendment.

APPLY Tell students that four of the ten amendments in the Bill of Rights protect a person's rights before, during, and after an arrest. Divide the class into four groups. Assign one of the amendments described on SE p. 108 to each group. Have the groups use the information in the text to write a version of the amendment that could be understood by other middle grades students. Have each group present and explain its version of the amendment to the class. Address any errors or important omissions after each presentation.

L1 Make sure students understand what it means to say that a government has power. Explain that one definition of *power* is "control over other people and their actions." Discuss some examples of situations in which one person has more power than another—a parent and a child, an employer and an employee, or a teacher and a student.

L2 Have students make a four-column chart titled Bill of Rights. The headings of the columns should be Fourth, Fifth, Sixth, and Eighth. Have students list a main idea and at least two supporting details for each amendment.

L4 Have students research the Magna Carta and compare the rights granted by King John in 1215 with the rights guaranteed by the Bill of Rights.

Build Inquiry: A Bill of Wrongs

TIME 20 minutes

TEACH Tell students that sometimes they can test their understanding of a concept by considering its opposite. For example, discuss what could happen if people were not protected from unreasonable searches. (*Sample answer:* The police could conduct a search at any time or place.)

APPLY Divide students into small groups. Ask each group to use the information on SE p. 108 to write a Bill of Wrongs—a list of what might happen if people did not have the rights listed in Amendments IV, V, VI, and VIII.

Background

RIGHT TO PRIVACY The Fourth Amendment applies only when a person has a legitimate expectation of privacy. For example, people at airports expect that their luggage may be searched because of the history of terrorism on planes. People who travel by bus don't expect their luggage to be searched.

You may want to tell students that the Fourth Amendment does not currently apply to private security guards, such as those at a shopping mall. Evidence found in a search by a private security guard can be turned over to police and used in court.

Monitor Progress

L3 **ORAL PRESENTATION** Write words or phrases such as *constitution, Bill of Rights, search warrant, double jeopardy, jury, bail,* and *Miranda warning* on slips of paper. Place the slips in a container and ask students to draw a slip and explain, without referring to their textbook, what the word or phrase means.

EL **ORAL PRESENTATION** Do the same exercise, but allow students to work with a partner who is proficient in English.

Types of Crimes SE p. 109

Teach Key Concepts: Classification of Crimes

L3 **FOCUS** Explain that a society cannot function without rules. As an example, use the rules that drivers and pedestrians have to follow. Discuss what could happen, for example, if there were no traffic lights or stop signs at intersections. Note that rules help protect both people and property.

TEACH Tell students that some laws define which actions are crimes. **Q:** How are crimes classified? **A:** as felonies and misdemeanors **Q:** In general, how do felonies differ from misdemeanors? **A:** Felonies are more serious crimes with more serious punishments.

APPLY As a class, make a list of school rules on the board. Discuss the punishments that could be meted out for violations of rules (detention, suspension, expulsion). Have students classify the rules into categories based on the severity of the punishment. Note that these lists can serve as an analogy for the classification of crimes as felonies and misdemeanors.

L2 Most local papers have police logs. Use the logs to judiciously select about a dozen appropriate examples. Include some probable felonies, some probable misdemeanors, and some activities where no one will be charged with a crime. Briefly describe each activity to students and have them decide whether it would be a felony or a misdemeanor, or neither.

Address Misconceptions: Pranks Can Be Crimes

FOCUS Ask students if they have observed someone doing a prank on Halloween or at other times. (Be clear that you don't want to know the names of the culprits.) Have students describe what they observed. Then ask if they think that these actions could be classified as crimes, and why.

TEACH Explain that actions that involve destruction of private or public property are considered crimes. If the people who caused the damage are caught, they can be punished for their actions.

APPLY Refer students to Figure 2 on SE p. 109. **Q:** What do you observe in the photograph on the right? **A:** A wall of a building is covered with graffiti. **Q:** When would spray painting a wall of a building be considered a misdemeanor? **A:** when the painters do not own the property or do not have the owner's permission

Background

JAILS AND PRISONS A jail is a short-term detention center. Some inmates in jail are waiting for a bond to be posted. Some have been convicted of a crime and sentenced to serve less than one year. A prison is a state or federal facility that houses felons whose sentence is longer than one year.

Answers

FIGURE 2 There was a surveillance camera in the store and investigators made a still photo from the video.

READING CHECKPOINT (SE p. 109) Laws are rules that everyone in society is supposed to follow.

Making an Arrest SE p. 110

Teach Key Concepts: Probable Cause

L3 **FOCUS** Remind students that *probable* means "likely to exist, occur, or be true."

TEACH Begin the discussion of probable cause by explaining that police officers need a reason to arrest a person. They need to believe that the person has committed a crime and they need to base that opinion on facts. Facts could be observations made by police officers or eyewitnesses. Facts also could be the results of tests run on evidence collected at a crime scene.

APPLY Have students work with a partner. Ask each team to read the first two paragraphs in the "Probable Cause" section on SE p. 110. Then have them list the observations and inferences that police used in each case as probable cause to make an arrest. (In the first case, they saw the suspect running from the building. They inferred that the suspect had broken into the building and set off the alarm. In the second case, either an eyewitness or an informant identified the robber. The police inferred that the identification was accurate and reliable.)

EL Pair English language learners with native speakers.

L4 Have students use the text of the Fourth Amendment to demonstrate that this amendment applies to arrest warrants.

Help Students Read: Use Prior Knowledge

L2 Have students reread the second paragraph about search warrants on SE p. 51. Then ask the following questions. **Q:** Based on the definition of a search warrant, how would you define an arrest warrant? **A:** An arrest warrant is a written court document that allows police to arrest a suspect. **Q:** What must police show to obtain a search warrant? **A:** They must show that their planned search is reasonable. **Q:** What must police show to obtain an arrest warrant? **A:** They must show that they have a reasonable belief that the person has committed a crime. **Q:** In both cases, what do police use to support their request for a warrant? **A:** They use evidence that they have gathered. Remind students that the evidence used to obtain a warrant could be direct evidence, physical evidence, or a combination.

Answers

FIGURE 3 The man being arrested has been handcuffed.

READING CHECKPOINT (SE p. 110) They need evidence that points to a particular person.

Pretrial Procedures SE pp. 111–112

Teach Key Concepts: Pretrial Hearings

L3 **FOCUS** Tell students that a person who is arrested may appear in court one or more times at a pretrial hearing.

TEACH Introduce the four key roles at a pretrial hearing—the defendant, the judge, the prosecutor, and the defense lawyer. **Q:** Who decides which crime or crimes a defendant will be charged with? **A:** the prosecutor **Q:** What must a defendant do when the charges are read in court? **A:** plead guilty or not guilty **Q:** What happens if a defendant cannot afford a lawyer? **A:** The judge will assign a lawyer to the case. **Q:** What happens if a judge doesn't want to release a defendant on bail? **A:** A hearing will be held to decide if the defendant is too dangerous to be released. **Q:** What must the prosecutor do if the defense asks a judge to dismiss a case for lack of evidence? **A:** persuade the judge that there is enough evidence to go ahead with the case

APPLY Have students review the case of the stolen dog on SE pp. 54–55. Say that Eva has been charged with burglary. Divide the class into small groups. Have each group prepare a skit in which a defense lawyer argues that the judge should dismiss the case against Eva for lack of evidence and the prosecutor argues that there is sufficient evidence to go to trial.

L2 Have students use the information in the sections with blue heads on SE pages 111–112 to summarize what could happen in each situation. For example, a defendant may be released without bail, be released with bail, or not be released.

Use Visuals: Figure 5

L3 **FOCUS** Explain that many criminal cases never get to trial. Often the prosecution and the defense reach an agreement that allows the defendant to plead guilty to a lesser charge with a lighter punishment.

TEACH Ask students to look at the possible charges in Figure 5. Explain that in all four cases the defendant is accused of killing a person. Ask students, based on the descriptions, which two variables can be used to classify a violent crime. (planning and intent) Explain that a prosecutor will consider these variables when determining the charge for a crime.

APPLY Explain that a burglary may involve unlawful entry (e.g., an unlocked door), forcible entry (e.g., a locked door), and attempted forcible entry. Ask students how these variables might affect the punishment. Also ask whether it might matter if the owners are home at the time of the burglary, and why.

EL Explain that *voluntary* and *involuntary* come from a Latin word meaning "to be willing" and that the prefix *in-* means "not."

L1 Make a large-print version of Figure 5 for visually-impaired students.

L4 Divide students into small groups. Ask each group to discuss these questions. If there were no plea bargains, what could happen to the courts? What would happen to a defendant's right to a speedy trial? Why did the people who wrote and approved the Bill of Rights think that having jury trials was important? Reconvene as a class to discuss the results.

Skills Activity **Making Judgments** SE p. 111

TIME 10 minutes

TEAM SIZE individual

EXPECTED OUTCOME Students should understand that a judge considers many factors when setting bail. Students should give reasonable explanations for their rankings.

TIPS Review what bail is and what protection the Eighth Amendment provides relative to bail. Ask students if bail that is set at $250,000 would be reasonable. The answer is that it depends on the crime and the resources available to the defendant.

Answers

FIGURE 5 involuntary manslaughter

Assess

Reviewing Key Concepts

1. a. the right to have an attorney even if the person can't afford one
   b. These amendments protect the rights of people who are accused of crimes before, during, and after an arrest.
   c. The person is more likely to get a fair trial with a lawyer because a lawyer is trained to represent a person in court.
2. a. felonies and misdemeanors
   b. *Sample answer:* A crime that involves a weapon is classified as a felony because there is the chance that people will be hurt.
3. a. charges against the defendant, bail, the need for a defense lawyer, and evidence
   b. The judge controls what takes place at a pretrial hearing.
   c. The defendant must plead guilty or not guilty to the charges.

Reteach

L2 Tell students that you will be playing the role of a judge and that you may need their help figuring out what to do at a pretrial hearing. Explain that a prosecutor, a defendant, and a defense lawyer are in the courtroom. Ask students what is likely to happen first. (The charges will be read.) Ask what will happen next. (The defendant will enter a plea.) Continue questioning the students about the issues discussed at pretrial hearings.

Performance Assessment

L3 **SKILLS CHECK** Tell students that police arrested a bank robber. Describe a series of events that might take place after the arrest and ask students how the robber's rights would be protected at each stage in the process.

In the Community: Comparing Rights

Encourage students to share what they have learned without violating the privacy of family members.

Lesson 4-2 SE pp. 113–120

Presenting Evidence in a Trial

Reading Preview

OBJECTIVES

After this lesson, students will be able to

4.2.1 Compare the assigned roles of a judge, an impartial jury, and the lawyers at a criminal trial.

4.2.2 Identify ways that lawyers use exhibits in court.

4.2.3 Explain how lawyers use witnesses to present evidence.

KEY TERMS

- bailiff
- exhibit
- testimony
- cross-examination
- expert witness

Target Reading Skill: Previewing Visuals

Explain that visuals contain important information. They can reinforce or extend concepts that are presented in the text. Using visuals to pose questions gives students a reason to read.

SAMPLE ANSWERS

Students may include the following answers.

QUESTION	ANSWER
What does a bailiff do?	A bailiff helps keep order in the court.
What does the court clerk do?	The court clerk keeps a schedule of cases and makes notes about each case.
What does a court reporter do?	The court reporter makes a record of everything that the lawyers, judge, and witnesses say.

DIFFERENTIATED INSTRUCTION KEY

Use this key as you review the instructional strategies.

- **L1** For students with special needs
- **L2** For less proficient readers
- **L3** For all students
- **L4** For gifted and talented students
- **EL** For English language learners

Preteach

Build Background Knowledge: Fiction vs. Fact

Explain that in this lesson students will learn how a trial is conducted. Ask students to suggest ways that an actual trial might differ from a trial in a movie or television drama. Use questions such as the following to generate discussion. Would an actual trial be as dramatic, start to finish, as a fictional trial? Would it be longer or shorter? What things happen in fictional trials that are less likely to happen in actual trials?

Discover Activity **What Makes a Good Juror?** SE p. 113

SKILLS FOCUS Making Judgments

TIME 10 minutes

TEAM SIZE pair

EXPECTED OUTCOME Students should realize the importance of having jurors who are not biased.

THINK IT OVER *Sample answer:* Having a connection to the defendant or a lawyer can make it difficult for a person to be fair. A person might form an opinion about a case based on news stories. People who assume that most defendants are guilty may be biased in favor of the prosecution.

Instruct

In the Courtroom SE p. 114

Teach Key Concepts: Roles in a Courtroom

L3 **FOCUS** Ask students to name places where people have assigned seats. (Possible answers include a classroom, a wedding, the U.S. Congress, and a ballpark.) Explain that a courtroom is organized so that people have assigned places according to their roles.

TEACH Refer students to Figure 6 on SE p. 114. Explain that most courtrooms have a similar arrangement. **Q:** Where does the judge sit? **A:** at the front of the court on a raised bench **Q:** Where do the lawyers sit? **A:** at tables facing the judge's bench

APPLY Tell students that some of the people in the courtroom are there to help the judge. Ask students what kind of help a judge might need. Then explain the roles of the bailiff, court clerk, and court reporter.

EL Ask what would happen if a defendant or a witness does not speak English. (There would have to be an interpreter in the courtroom.)

L1 Build a three-dimensional courtroom model for visually-impaired students based on Figure 6.

Answers

FIGURE 6 The defense lawyer and the defendant sit at one table and the prosecutor sits at another. The tables are placed so the lawyers and the defendant face the judge and the witness stand.

A Jury Is Chosen SE p. 115

Teach Key Concepts: Selecting an Impartial Jury

L3 **FOCUS** Say that a coach is holding tryouts for a basketball team. **Q:** What physical traits or abilities would the coach look for in the players? **A:** *Sample answer:* height, speed, strength, and vertical jump **Q:** What nonphysical traits might the coach look for? **A:** The coach might want players who pay attention, follow the rules, and cooperate. Explain that these nonphysical traits can also apply to jurors.

TEACH Review the minimum requirements for jurors—citizens who are age 18 or older and live in the district where the court is located. Then discuss the selection process. Stress the need to have a jury pool that is representative of the community and jurors who will be fair.

APPLY Explain that the questions listed in the Discover Activity on SE p. 113 are general enough to be asked in any trial, but lawyers must also ask questions related to a specific trial. Pair up students. Write scenarios such as the following on the board, and ask students to think of at least one question a lawyer might want to ask a potential juror. (1) The defendant is accused of cruelty to animals. (Do you have any pets? Do you volunteer at an animal shelter?) (2) The defendant is accused of a bank robbery. (Do you work in a bank? Have you ever been robbed?)

L2 Develop of list of adjectives that are synonyms of the word *impartial*, such as *neutral, fair, evenhanded,* and *balanced*.

L4 Explain that a defendant also has rights based on the Fourteenth Amendment. Discuss how the practice of excluding people from juries based on race could affect a defendant's right to a fair trial.

Teach the Big Idea

Build Inquiry: Juror Profiles

TIME 30 minutes

MATERIALS 3″× 5″ index cards

ADVANCE PREPARATION Use the cards to make a set of 36 juror profiles. Include data such as age, gender, marital status, number of children (if any), level of education, and type of occupation (including homemaker). Add one or two specific facts about each person that might be of interest to the defense lawyer or prosecutor in the Bruno Hauptmann trial.

FOCUS Read aloud the Big Idea question for this chapter. Explain that one way to ensure a fair trial is to have a variety of people on a jury.

TEACH Have students reread the story of Bruno Hauptmann on SE p. 96. Select 12 cards at random from the jury pool. Read each profile and ask students to decide whether the prosecutor or the defense lawyer might challenge this juror. Ask students to state a reason for excluding a juror. Select cards from the jury pool to replace excluded jurors until 12 jurors have been selected.

APPLY Have 12 students volunteer to be questioned as potential jurors. Give each volunteer an index card. Let other students ask questions and have the jurors respond based on the profile on their index cards.

Skills Activity — Calculating SE p.115

TIME 10 minutes

TEAM SIZE individual

L3 **TIPS** Review the definition of *probability* from SE p. 92. Tell students to report their answers as a percentage. Remind students that 12 jurors are needed for one trial.

EXPECTED OUTCOME
12 divided by 150 = 8 percent

L1 Review how to decide which number to put in the numerator and which to put in the denominator of a ratio.

Answers

READING CHECKPOINT (SE p. 115) citizens who are age 18 or older who live in the district where the trial is being held

The Lawyers Argue the Case SE p. 116

Teach Key Concepts: The Adversarial Process

L3 **FOCUS** Explain that another way to ensure a fair trial is to use an adversary system for presenting evidence at trial. Explain that an adversary is a person who opposes or fights against another.

TEACH Explain that the adversaries, or opponents, in a trial are the prosecutor and defense attorney. **Q:** What is the prosecutor's goal? **A:** to convince the jury that the defendant is guilty **Q:** What is the defense lawyer's goal? **A:** to convince the jury that that the prosecutor has not proven his case

Discuss how lawyers use their opening statements to begin to accomplish their goals. **Q:** What does a prosecutor try to accomplish in his opening statement? **A:** He states his hypothesis about what the defendant did, and why. He may preview the evidence that he intends to present to support his hypothesis. **Q:** What does the defense lawyer try to accomplish in her opening statement? **A:** She points out weak points in the prosecutor's case, and may offer an opposing hypothesis.

APPLY Ask students to compare what lawyers do in a trial to what opposing sides do in a debate. (In both a debate and a trial, there are people who represent the opposing positions. Each side uses its persuasive skills to convince listeners that its position is right. Each side also highlights facts that support its side of the question.)

L2 Provide students with a scenario such as the following. Tiki and Ted are roommates. When Tiki opens his wallet to pay for a pizza delivery, he finds less money than he expected. He accuses Ted of stealing money from his wallet. Ted claims he is innocent. Ask students to suggest a hypothesis Ted can offer to counter Tiki's accusation. (Possible answers include that Tiki is mistaken about how much money he had, or that there was no time when Ted was alone in the apartment with access to the wallet.)

Answers

FIGURE 8 The jury, not the judge, decides whether the defendant is guilty or not guilty.

READING CHECKPOINT (SE p. 116) A prosecutor develops a hypothesis to explain the evidence.

Visual Evidence SE p. 117

Teach Key Concepts: Uses of Exhibits

L3 **FOCUS** Discuss the types of exhibits students use at a science fair and how these exhibits make it easier for participants to explain their projects to the judges. Explain that some exhibits that lawyers use in court are similar to the exhibits used at a science fair. Others are pieces of physical evidence that were collected at a crime scene or at related locations such as a suspect's home.

TEACH Write the three blue heads from SE p. 117 on the board. Ask students to use what they learned in previous chapters to suggest types of items that could be used as exhibits to accomplish each goal. Challenge students to think of examples that are not listed in the text. (a floor plan to show locations at an indoor crime scene; a surveillance video or forensic artist's sketch to connect a suspect to a crime, and a photo with labels to explain why fingerprints are a match)

APPLY Return to the case of the stolen dog. Have groups of students decide what exhibits a prosecutor might use at Jada's trial. Encourage students to consider both evidence described in the text and other evidence that a CSI might have collected. (*Sample answer:* Jada's sweater and shoes; dog hairs; photos or charts showing the results of tests run on hairs, soil, and glass; a photo of a shoe print left in the spilled soil)

L1 Note that jurors (or other trial participants) may be visually or hearing impaired. Stress that visual exhibits are never used on their own. There is always a witness who can describe the exhibit. Courts may hire a person to read aloud documents. They may use closed captioning or a sign language interpreter. People who interpret, write captions, or read documents must take an oath to do their jobs accurately without any bias.

Answers

READING CHECKPOINT (SE p. 117) A lawyer can use enlarged photos and drawings, a video, or a scale model.

FIGURE 9 The witness is using an aerial photograph of a neighborhood.

Oral Evidence SE pp. 118–120

Teach Key Concepts: The Testimony of Witnesses

L3 **FOCUS** Explain that a lawyer uses witnesses to present evidence, including exhibits, at trial.

TEACH Note that the lawyer who calls a witness does a direct examination. **Q:** What is a leading question? **A:** a question that contains the answer the lawyer wants **Q:** What is a cross-examination? **A:** the process in which a lawyer questions another lawyer's witness **Q:** Why do you think lawyers can ask leading questions during a cross-examination? **A:** *Sample answer:* The witness may be reluctant to volunteer information that would help the defendant. Note that the questions asked during a cross-examination must be related to facts introduced during the direct examination. **Q:** Why do you think lawyers ask questions they know will bring an objection? **A:** *Sample answer:* The jury will hear and remember the question even if the judge tells them to ignore it.

APPLY Explain that part of a prosecutor's strategy, or plan, for presenting a case is to decide on the sequence of questions to ask a witness. Ask students to suggest a general sequence of questions for a prosecutor to ask an expert witness who is called to testify about DNA evidence. (*Sample answer:* (1) the expert's qualifications, (2) the structure of DNA and how a DNA profile is made, (3) the probability of two people having the same DNA profile, and (4) the specific evidence in the case.)

L1 Discuss why witnesses are asked to swear to tell the truth. Talk about what could happen, to both the witnesses and the defendant, if witnesses were to lie.

L4 Ask pairs of students to make decision trees for the first five moves they would use if they were playing a game such as checkers (or tic-tac-toe). Have students begin to play the game. Ask them to adjust their decision trees after each move as needed. Discuss how these changes in strategy are similar to what lawyers must do during a trial.

Chapter 4

Skills Activity — Posing Questions SE p. 119

TIME 10 minutes

TEAM SIZE individual

TIPS Remind students that the defense lawyer wants to ask questions that cast doubt on the testimony of the witness.

EXPECTED OUTCOME The questions should be related to the stated facts. Possible questions include: "How far were you from the fire escape?" "At any time, was the person facing you?" "Isn't it true that the street light near the fire escape was broken?"

Answers

FIGURE 10 *Sample answer:* The lawyer appears calm and friendly.

FIGURE 11 *Sample answer:* The lawyer may be aggressive and challenge the witness.

READING CHECKPOINT (SE p. 119) The goal of cross-examination is to make the testimony of a witness appear less believable.

Assess

Reviewing Key Concepts

1. a. The judge makes sure everyone in the courtroom behaves and follows the law. The judge acts as a referee when the opposing lawyers disagree. The prosecutor tries to convince the jury that the defendant is guilty. The defense lawyer tries to give the jury at least one reason to doubt what the prosecutor says.
   b. An impartial jury decides a case based only on the evidence.
   c. *Sample answer:* Do you have children, and if so, how old are they?
2. a. An exhibit is a physical object that is used to make a point in court.
   b. Lawyers use exhibits to present a crime scene, connect a defendant to a crime, or explain scientific evidence.
   c. *Sample answer:* the prosecutor, who has both visual records and evidence from the crime scene
3. a. Witnesses provide oral evidence, or testimony.
   b. The lawyer who calls a witness does the direct examination. The opposing lawyer does the cross-examination.
   c. The lawyer isn't doing a direct examination because ordinarily lawyers cannot ask leading questions during a direct examination.

Reteach

L2 Make a chart with four columns headed Judge, Jury, Lawyer, and Witness. Ask students to volunteer things they learned that they did not know about each category.

Performance Assessment

L3 **WRITING** Have students compare and contrast the roles of a prosecutor and a defense lawyer.

L2 **ORAL PRESENTATION** Have students describe how a jury is selected.

At-Home Activity: Mapping Justice

Choose an area that should be included in the map (single community, county, and so on) and determine what type of map would be most useful as a base map. Obtain printed maps such as street maps, realtor's maps, or tourist maps. Or download maps such as Zip code maps or USGS maps. Help students search online for sites that show the location of correction facilities or courthouses. You may want to do this project as a class activity.

Skills Lab Making a Scale Model SE p. 121

KEY CONCEPT

Lawyers use exhibits to present a crime scene, connect a defendant to a crime, or explain scientific evidence.

SKILLS OBJECTIVE

After this lab, students will be able to

- calculate an appropriate scale for a model.
- use a scale to determine the size and placement of objects in a model.
- construct a scale model.

CLASS TIME 45 minutes

TEAM SIZE small group

See pp. 137–138 in the Student Handbook, ATE for additional information.

Forensics & Technology

Modeling a Crime Scene

SE pp. 122–123

Background The laser scanner can quickly record a large amount of data. The raw data, or point cloud, is precise to within a few millimeters. The data is displayed as a graphical image. A technician uses a software program to connect the points in a triangulated mesh. The program's "edge detection" algorithms identify the outlines of objects. Before the data file is exported to other applications, the file size is reduced by deleting points that are not needed to display an accurate model.

If the focus of an investigation shifts, a surveyor doesn't need to return to the site because the scanner recorded every object within view during the initial survey.

Build Inquiry

LASERS

MATERIALS flashlight, laser pointer, tennis ball, measuring tape, stopwatch

TEACH Point a flashlight and a laser at a dark surface. Have students compare the width of the beams.

Use a tennis ball to model the reflection of laser light. Use a wall without windows. Measure distances from the wall of 5, 10, and 15 m. Have a student standing at the 5-m mark throw the ball at the wall. Have a second student measure the time it takes the ball to travel to the wall and back. Repeat at 10 m and 15 m. Have students describe the distance–time relation. Explain that the relation is the same for a laser, but the times are much quicker.

Go Online

FOR Links on lasers
VISIT www.SciLinks.org
WEB CODE dan-1040

Download a worksheet for students.

Background

HOW A LASER WORKS

Laser is short for light amplification by stimulated emission of radiation. To *amplify* means to increase, in this case the energy of the light.

A laser tube contains inert gases. When an electric current is passed through the gases, their atoms emit packets of energy called photons. Mirrors at both ends of the tube reflect the photons back and forth. When a photon strikes an atom, the atom emits a photon with the same energy as the photon that struck the atom. The process continues until there is a stream of photons with the same energy moving up and down the tube. Some energy is able to pass through a mirror at one end of the tube. This is the laser beam. Its waves are coherent, meaning they all have the same wavelength.

Teacher Demo

3-D PANORAMAS

TEACH Search online for "full screen panoramas." Project a few images. Ask students how a 360° view can increase a viewer's understanding of a scene. (A viewer can see all aspects of a scene.) Zoom in on an image and ask what advantage this view provides. (A viewer can see details that are not visible in the long-range view.)

APPLY Ask students to apply what they learned to the use of 3-D crime scene models.

Writing in Science

ECHOLOCATION

Have students research how bats find their prey and write a paragraph comparing the process to laser scanning. (The bat emits sound. When the sound reflects off the prey, the bat's brain uses the time elapsed to determine the distance to the prey.)

You Be the Judge

1. *Sample answer:* A lawyer might want to show what witnesses were able to see from their locations.
2. Answers should note that the goal is the same, but using a laser provides more data. The laser is also faster and more accurate.
3. *Sample answer:* Laser scan technology is too expensive for most trials.

Chapter 4

Lesson 4-3 SE pp. 124–128

The Final Stages of a Trial

Reading Preview

OBJECTIVES

After this lesson, students will be able to

4.3.1 Describe the process a jury uses to reach a verdict.
4.3.2 State what happens when a person is found guilty.

KEY TERMS

• verdict • foreperson • probation • appeal

Target Reading Skill: Relating Cause and Effect

Explain that a cause is the reason something happens. The effect is the result of what happens. Explain that sometimes a cause can have more than one effect.

SAMPLE ANSWERS

Students may include the following answers.

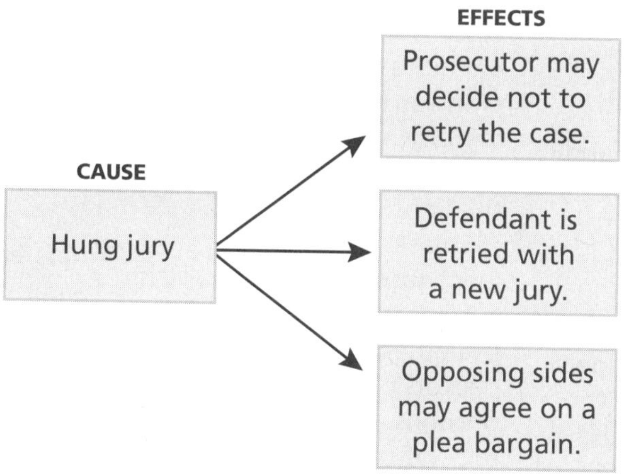

EFFECTS
Prosecutor may decide not to retry the case.
CAUSE
Hung jury
Defendant is retried with a new jury.
Opposing sides may agree on a plea bargain.

DIFFERENTIATED INSTRUCTION KEY

Use this key as you review the instructional strategies.

- **L1** For students with special needs
- **L2** For less proficient readers
- **L3** For all students
- **L4** For gifted and talented students
- **EL** For English language learners

Preteach

Build Background Knowledge: Reaching Consensus

As a class, make a list of situations in which two or more people would need to agree on a decision. Discuss the methods people use to reach an agreement, or consensus. Stress that a jury must also find a may to reach an agreement.

Discover Activity Is the Evidence Persuasive? SE p. 124

SKILLS FOCUS Posing Questions

TIME 10 minutes

TEAM SIZE pair

TIPS A marked bill is a bill whose serial number was recorded or a bill that was tagged in some way to distinguish it from other bills. Ask if Statements 1 and 3 could both be true. (yes, if the witness made an honest error)

EXPECTED OUTCOME Students may conclude that jurors must make judgments about the evidence presented at a trial.

THINK IT OVER *Sample answer:* Did the witness have a clear view of the kidnapper's face? Did the defendant have more than one marked bill? How is the alibi witness related to the defendant?

Instruct

The Case Goes to the Jury SE pp. 125–126

Teach Key Concepts: How a Jury Reaches a Verdict

L3 **FOCUS** Remind students that a jury must base its decision on the evidence presented by the lawyers during the trial.

TEACH Ask the following questions. **Q:** What is the decision in a trial called? **A:** a verdict **Q:** What is the role of the foreperson? **A:** The foreperson manages the discussion. **Q:** What is a unanimous verdict? **A:** a verdict on which all 12 jurors agree **Q:** What is a hung jury? **A:** a jury that cannot agree on a verdict

APPLY Ask students whether they think what happens in the jury room is a debate, and why. Then explain that what takes place in a jury room isn't a debate. It is a deliberation. During a deliberation, people consider and discuss alternative positions before reaching a decision.

L2 Explain that words such as *deliberation* and *deliberately* come from a Latin word meaning "to consider" or "weigh." A person who acts deliberately is unhurried and methodical.

L4 In Latin, *libra* means "scales." Ask students to research the relationship of scales and the justice system.

Background

SOCRATES' TRIAL Socrates was accused of impiety and corruption of youth. After the charges were read, the accusers had three hours to make their case. Socrates had three hours to respond. Part of the oath sworn by the jurors can be translated as: "I will vote only on the matters raised in the charge, and I will listen impartially to the accusers and defenders alike."

Math Analyzing Data — Sentences for Felony Convictions SE p. 126

MATH SKILL Interpreting Graphs

FOCUS Use this activity as a transition between discussions of jury deliberation and sentencing. Review the definition of a felony and explain the range of sentences that are available when a defendant is found guilty of a felony.

TEACH Remind students to study the graph before trying to answer the questions.

ANSWERS

1. about 30 percent in both years
2. more are sentenced to prison
3. about 70 percent
4. about 70 percent, if the trends shown on the graph held
5. about 400,000
6. *Sample answer:* The number increased based on the additional space available.

Answers

FIGURE 13 *Sample answer:* The room provides a private space where jurors can speak freely without fear of having their remarks overheard. Plus jurors are less likely to be distracted.

READING CHECKPOINT (SE p. 126) In a unanimous verdict, all jurors agree.

Sentences and Appeals SE pp. 127–128

Teach Key Concepts: Choosing a Punishment

L3 **FOCUS** Remind students that once a defendant is found guilty the judge must determine a punishment.

TEACH Explain that a judge often has a range of punishments to choose from. The judge will receive advice from the lawyers, but the final decision belongs to the judge. The most important factor a judge must consider is the seriousness of the crime. The judge will also consider whether the defendant has been convicted of other crimes.

Explain that a defendant who is found guilty may appeal the verdict. **Q:** What is an appeal? **A:** a written request that the verdict in a trial be reversed **Q:** Where is the appeal sent? **A:** to the next highest court in the system **Q:** Is a lawyer allowed to present new evidence in an appeal? **A:** no, only mistakes that a judge made during trial that may have affected the verdict

APPLY Review the types of sentences. Present the following scenarios. Ask students to classify the crime, decide on a sentence, and explain why. **Q:** A defendant with no previous record is found guilty of painting graffiti on a public building. **A:** misdemeanor, probation, first offense **Q:** A defendant who is a convicted thief is found guilty of stealing a car. **A:** felony, jail, not first offense **Q:** A defendant with no previous record is found guilty of second degree murder. **A:** felony, prison, serious crime

Answers

FIGURE 14 The defendant will be freed.

Assess

Reviewing Key Concepts

1. **a.** The judge instructs the jury; the jurors meet to discuss the evidence; the jurors vote on a verdict; if necessary, the jurors discuss and vote several more times.
   b. The prosecutor may decide not to retry the case; the prosecutor may retry the case with a new jury; or the lawyers may reach a plea bargain.
   c. *Sample answer:* The foreperson can keep the jury focused on the task.
2. **a.** The judge must decide on a punishment, or sentence. The defense must decide whether to appeal the verdict.
   b. *Sample answer:* The victim may want the defendant to understand the consequences of his or her actions. He or she may also want to influence the sentence.
   c. No. An appeal can be based only on mistakes made by the judge during the trial that had an effect on the verdict.

Reteach

L2 Have students identify a main idea and at least two supporting details for the paragraphs within each blue heading.

Performance Assessment

L3 **WRITING** Have students pretend they are a judge and have them write a paragraph with instructions for a jury.

L2 **DRAWING** Have students make a flowchart showing the sequence of events from closing arguments to a verdict being read in the courtroom.

Writing in Science

WRITING MODE: Summary

SCORING RUBRIC

4	Exceeds criteria: a well-written, well-organized, detailed description of the process
3	Meets criteria: provides detailed information about the process
2	Too general; provides few details about the process
1	Ineffective; description is minimal

Chapter Project

KEEP STUDENTS ON TRACK By now, students should have finished their planning and participated in the mock trial.

Chapter 4

Chapter 4 Chapter Review

Study Guide SE p. 129

Apply the Big Idea

Connect to Key Concepts
Reinforce the Big Idea by connecting it to important Key Concepts. For example, ask: Why is it important that a defendant have a lawyer? (If the prosecutor's case isn't challenged, jurors may not realize that the evidence presented doesn't prove guilt beyond a reasonable doubt.)

Connecting to Key Terms
Reinforce the chapter's Big Idea by having students connect Key Terms to the concept of a fair trial. For example, for *jury*, students could say that a jury must be impartial. For *appeal*, students could say that the appeal process gives the defense a chance to challenge errors made by the judge.

Review and Assessment SE pp. 130–131

Organizing Information

a. Fourth
b. Rights of the Accused
c. Right to remain silent
d. Right to a Jury Trial
e. Right to have a lawyer
f. Cruel or unusual punishment

Reviewing Key Terms

1. d 2. c 3. b 4. a
5. False; judge 6. True
7. False; cross-examination
8. True 9. False; probation

Writing in Science

WRITING MODE: DEBATE

SCORING RUBRIC

4	Exceeds criteria: Well-written; provides three valid points (e.g., presumed innocent, Sixth Amendment, prosecutor must prove case)
3	Meets criteria: provides three valid points
2	Provides fewer than three points or points that are not valid
1	Does not address the question

Checking Concepts

10. The Bill of Rights protects the rights of a defendant before, during, and after an arrest.
11. A felony is a more serious crime; it usually has a longer sentence than a misdemeanor.
12. *Sample answer:* Police will record information about the suspect, take mug shots, and take fingerprints.
13. The reporter keeps a record of everything that is said by the judge, lawyers, and witnesses. The clerk keeps a schedule of cases, makes a summary of what happens, swears in witnesses, and keeps a list of exhibits.
14. With a greater variety of people, there is a better chance that the jury will be fair.
15. Lawyers use visual evidence to recreate a crime scene, link a defendant to a crime, or help explain scientific evidence. They use oral evidence to present the observations of eyewitnesses and investigators. They also use oral evidence to introduce and explain exhibits.

Thinking Critically

16. Many people are not aware of their rights.
17. *Sample answer:* These documents give the police permission to act, but only after the police provide a reason for their actions.
18. Question b is a leading question because it contains the answer the lawyer wants the jury to hear.
19. The judge instructs the jury about the law and decides on the sentence. The jury considers the evidence and reaches a verdict.
20. *Sample answer:* Time and money are invested in a trial. Having to repeat the process can be costly. Plus there is no guarantee that a second jury will be able to reach a verdict.
21. The lawyer can appeal the case to the state supreme court.

Applying Skills

22. It increased dramatically; violent crime
23. about 1,250,000 people; about 20 percent
24. *Sample answer:* The guidelines are likely to increase the size of the prison population because judges have less control over the sentences.

Chapter Project

PERFORMANCE ASSESSMENT Evaluate students' ability to apply what they learned about the trial process to their assigned roles in the mock trial. Also ask students to evaluate the process. Have them select those parts of the process that they think were successful and those that they think needed improvement. Ask them to provide reasons for their selections.

Think Like a Scientist

SE pp. 132–133

The Skills Handbook is designed as a reference for students to use whenever they need to review inquiry, math, or reading skills. You can use the activities in the Skills Handbook to teach or reinforce skills.

Observing

FOCUS Remind students that an observation is what they can see, hear, smell, taste, or feel.

TEACH Invite students to make observations of the classroom. List these observations on the board. Challenge students to identify the senses they used to make each observation. **Q:** Which senses will you use to make observations from the photograph on page 132? **A:** Sight is the only sense that can be used to make observations from a photograph.

Activity Some observations that students might make include that the boy is skateboarding, wearing a white helmet, and flying in the air. Make sure that students' observations are confined to only things that they can actually see in the photograph.

Inferring

FOCUS Choose one or two of the classroom observations listed on the board, and ask students to interpret them.

TEACH Encourage students to describe their thought processes in making their inferences. Point out how they used their knowledge and experience to interpret the observations. Then invite students to suggest other possible interpretations for the observations. **Q:** How can you find out whether an inference is correct? **A:** by further investigation

Activity One possible inference is that the boy just skated off a ramp at a skate park. Invite students to share their experiences that helped them make the inference.

Predicting

FOCUS Discuss the weather forecast for the next day. Point out that this prediction is an inference about what will happen in the future based on observations and experience.

TEACH Help students differentiate between a prediction and an inference. You might organize the similarities and differences in a Venn diagram on the board. Both are interpretations of observations using experience and knowledge, and both can be incorrect. Inferences describe current or past events. Predictions describe future events.

Activity Students might predict that the boy will land and skate to the other side. Others might predict that the boy will fall. Students should also describe the evidence or experience on which they based their predictions.

Classifying

FOCUS Encourage students to think of common things that are classified.

TEACH Ask: **Q:** What things at home are classified? **A:** Clothing might be classified in order to place it in the appropriate dresser drawer; glasses, plates, and silverware are grouped in different parts of the kitchen; screws, nuts, bolts, washers, and nails might be separated into small containers. **Q:** What are some things that scientists classify? **A:** Scientists classify many things they study, including organisms, geological features and processes, and kinds of machines.

Activity Some characteristics students might use include color, pattern of color, use of balls, and size. Students' criteria for classification should clearly divide the balls into two, and then three, distinct groups.

Making Models

FOCUS Ask: **Q:** What are some models you have used to study science? **A:** Students might have used human anatomical models, solar system models, maps, or stream tables. **Q:** How have these models helped you? **A:** Models can help you learn about things that are difficult to study because they are very large, very small, or highly complex.

TEACH Be sure students understand that a model does not have to be three-dimensional. For example, a map is a model, as is an equation. Have students look at the photograph of the student modeling the causes of day and night on Earth. **Q:** What quality of each item makes this a good model? **A:** The flashlight gives off light, and the ball is round and can be rotated by the student.

Activity The flashlight represents the sun and the ball represents Earth.

Communicating

FOCUS Have students identify the methods of communication they have used today.

TEACH Ask: **Q:** How is the way you communicate with a friend similar to and different from the way scientists communicate about their work to other scientists? **A:** Both may communicate using various methods, but scientists must be very detailed and precise, whereas communication between friends may be less detailed and precise. Encourage students to communicate like a scientist as they carry out the shoe-tying activity.

Activity Students' answers will vary but should identify a step-by-step process for tying a shoe. Help students identify communication errors such as leaving out a step, putting steps in the wrong order, or disregarding the person's handedness.

Making Measurements SE pp. 134–135

Measuring in SI

FOCUS Review SI units with students. Begin by providing metric rulers, graduated cylinders, balances, and Celsius thermometers. Use these tools to reinforce that the meter is the unit of length, the liter is the unit of volume, the gram is the unit of mass, and the degree Celsius is the unit of temperature.

TEACH Ask: **Q:** If you want to measure the length and the width of the classroom, which SI unit would you use? **A:** meter **Q:** Which unit would you use to measure the amount of mass in your textbook? **A:** gram **Q:** Which would you use to measure how much water a drinking glass holds? **A:** liter **Q:** When would you use the Celsius scale? **A:** to measure the temperature of something

Then use the measuring equipment to review SI prefixes. For example, **Q:** What are the smallest units on the metric ruler? **A:** millimeters **Q:** How many millimeters are there in one centimeter? **A:** 10 millimeters **Q:** How many in 10 centimeters? **A:** 100 millimeters **Q:** How many centimeters are there in one meter? **A:** 100 centimeters **Q:** What does 1,000 meters equal? **A:** one kilometer

Activity **LENGTH** The length of the shell is 7.8 centimeters, or 78 millimeters. If students need more practice measuring length, have them use meter sticks and metric rulers to measure various objects in the classroom.

Activity **VOLUME** The volume of water in the graduated cylinder is 62 milliliters. If students need more practice, have them use a graduated cylinder to measure different volumes of water.

Activity **MASS** The mass of the potato is 0.25 kilograms. You would need 4 potatoes to make one kilogram. If students need more practice, give them various objects, such as coins, paper clips, and books, to measure mass.

Activity **TEMPERATURE** The temperature of the liquid is 35°C. Students who need more practice can measure the temperatures of various water samples.

Converting SI Units

FOCUS Review the steps for converting SI units, and work through the example with students.

TEACH Ask: **Q:** How many millimeters are in 80 centimeters? **A:** With the relationship 10 millimeters = 1 centimeter, students should follow the steps to calculate that 80 centimeters is equal to 800 millimeters.

Activity

1. 600 millimeters = 0.6 meters
2. 0.35 liters = 350 milliliters
3. 1,050 grams = 1.05 kilograms

If students need more practice converting SI units, have them make up conversion problems to trade with partners.

Conducting a Scientific Investigation SE pp. 136–137

Posing Questions

FOCUS Ask: **Q:** What do you do when you want to learn about something? **A:** Answers might include asking questions or looking for information in books or on the Internet. Explain that scientists go through the same process to learn about something.

TEACH Tell students that the questions scientists ask may have no answers or many different answers. To answer their questions, scientists often conduct experiments. **Q:** Why is a scientific question important to a scientific investigation? **A:** It helps the scientist decide if an experiment is necessary; the answer might already be known. It also helps focus the idea so that the scientist can form a hypothesis. **Q:** What is the scientific question in the activity on page 137? **A:** Is a ball's bounce affected by the height from which it is dropped?

Developing a Hypothesis

FOCUS Emphasize that a hypothesis is one possible explanation for a set of observations. It is not a guess. It is often based on an inference.

TEACH Ask: **Q:** On what information do scientists base their hypotheses? **A:** They use their observations and previous knowledge or experience. Point out that a hypothesis does not always turn out to be correct. **Q:** When a hypothesis turns out to be incorrect, do you think the scientist wasted his or her time? Explain. **A:** No. The scientist learned from the investigation and will develop another hypothesis that could prove to be correct.

Designing an Experiment

FOCUS Have a volunteer read the procedure in the box on page 137. Invite students to identify the manipulated variable (amount of salt), the variables kept constant (amount and temperature of water, location of containers), the control (Container 3), and the responding variable (time required for the water to freeze).

TEACH Ask: **Q:** How might the experiment be affected if Container 1 had only 100 milliliters of water? **A:** It would not be possible to draw a conclusion because there would be two manipulated variables—amount of water and amount of salt. Make sure that students understand the importance of the control. **Q:** What operational definition is used in this experiment? **A:** "Frozen" means the time at which a wooden stick can no longer move in a container.

Interpreting Data

FOCUS Ask: **Q:** What kind of data would you collect from the experiment with freezing salt water? **A:** time and state of the water

TEACH Ask: **Q:** What if you forgot to record some data during an investigation? **A:** You wouldn't be able to draw valid conclusions because some data are missing. **Q:** Why are data tables and graphs a good way to organize data? **A:** They make it easier to record data accurately, as well as compare and analyze data. **Q:** What kind of data table and graph might you use for this experiment? **A:** A table would have columns for each container with a row for each time interval in which the state of water is recorded. A bar graph would show the time elapsed until water froze for each container.

Drawing Conclusions

FOCUS Help students understand that a conclusion is not necessarily the end of a scientific investigation. A conclusion about one experiment may lead right into another experiment.

TEACH Point out that a conclusion in scientific investigations is a summary and explanation of the results of an experiment. For the procedure described on page 137, tell students to suppose that they obtained the following results: Container 1 froze in 45 minutes, Container 2 in 80 minutes, and Container 3 in 25 minutes. Then, ask: **Q:** What conclusions can you draw from this experiment? **A:** Students might conclude that water takes longer to freeze as more salt is added to it. The hypothesis is supported, and the question of which freezes faster is answered—fresh water.

Activity You might want to have students work in pairs to plan the controlled experiment. Students should develop a hypothesis, such as, "If I increase the height from which a ball is dropped, then the height of its bounce will increase." They can test the hypothesis by dropping a ball from varying heights (the manipulated variable). All trials should be done with the same kind of ball and on the same surface (constants). For each trial, they should measure the height of the bounce (responding variable). After students have designed the experiment, provide rubber balls, and invite them to carry out the experiment so they can collect and interpret data and draw conclusions.

Creating Data Tables and Graphs SE pp. 138–140

Data Tables

FOCUS Emphasize the importance of organizing data. **Q:** What might happen if you didn't use a data table for an experiment? **A:** Possible answers include that data might not be collected or they might be forgotten.

TEACH Have students create a data table to show how much time they spend on different activities during one week. Suggest that students first list the main activities they do every week. Then they should determine the amount of time they spend on each activity each day. Remind students to give the data table a title. See sample data table below.

Time Spent on Different Activities in a Week

	Going to Classes	Eating Meals	Playing Soccer	Watching Television
Monday	6	2	2	0.5
Tuesday	6	1.5	1.5	1.5
Wednesday	6	2	1	2
Thursday	6	2	2	1.5
Friday	6	2	2	0.5
Saturday	0	2.5	2.5	1
Sunday	0	3	1	2

Bar Graphs

FOCUS Have students compare and contrast the data table and the bar graph on page 138. **Q:** Why would you make a bar graph if the data are already organized in a table? **A:** The bar graph organizes the data in a visual way that makes them easier to interpret.

TEACH Students can use the data from the data table they created to make a bar graph that shows the amount of time they spend on different activities during a week. The vertical axis should be divided into units of time, such as hours. Remind students to label both axes and give their graph a title. A sample bar graph is shown below.

Time Spent on Different Activities in a Week

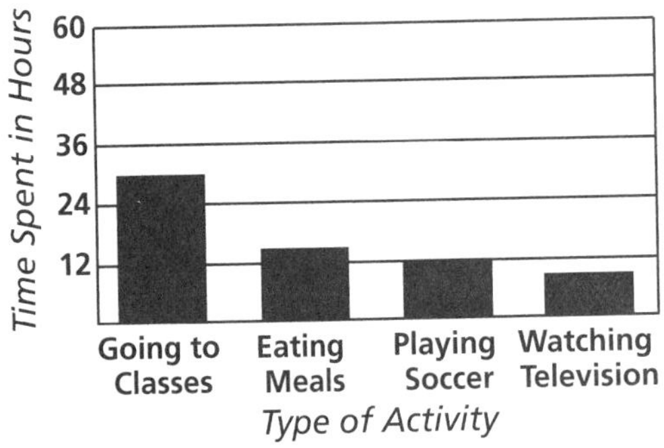

Line Graphs

FOCUS Ask: **Q:** Would a bar graph show the relationship between body mass and the number of Calories burned in 30 minutes? **A:** No. Bar graphs can only show data in distinct categories. Explain that line graphs are used to show how one variable changes in response to another variable.

TEACH Walk students through the steps involved in creating a line graph using the example on page 139. **Q:** What is the label on the horizontal axis? On the vertical axis? **A:** Body Mass (kg); Calories Burned in 30 Minutes **Q:** What scale is used on each axis? **A:** 10 kg on the *x*-axis and 20 Calories on the *y*-axis **Q:** What does the second data point represent? **A:** 77 Calories burned for a body mass of 40 kg **Q:** What trend or pattern does the graph show? **A:** The number of Calories burned in 30 minutes of cycling increases with body mass.

Activity Students should make a different graph for each experiment. Each graph should have a different *x*-axis scale that is appropriate for the data. See sample graphs.

Circle Graphs

FOCUS Emphasize that a circle graph must include 100 percent of the categories for the topic being graphed. Ask: **Q:** Could the data in the bar graph titled "Calories Burned by a 30-kilogram Person in Various Activities" be shown in a circle graph? Why or why not? **A:** No. It does not include all the possible ways a 30-kilogram person can burn Calories.

TEACH Walk students through the steps for making a circle graph. If necessary, help them with the compass and the protractor. Use the protractor to illustrate that a circle has 360 degrees. Make sure students understand the mathematical calculations involved in making a circle graph.

Activity You might have students work in pairs to complete the activity. Students' circle graphs should look like the sample graph.

Effect of Body Mass on Calories Burned While Playing Basketball

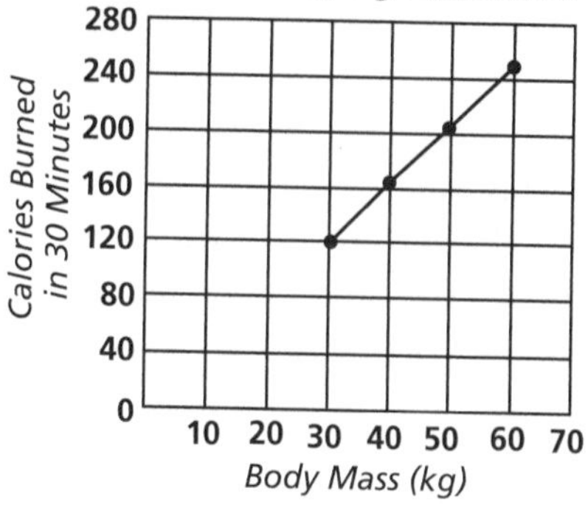

Effect of Body Mass on Calories Burned While Watching Television

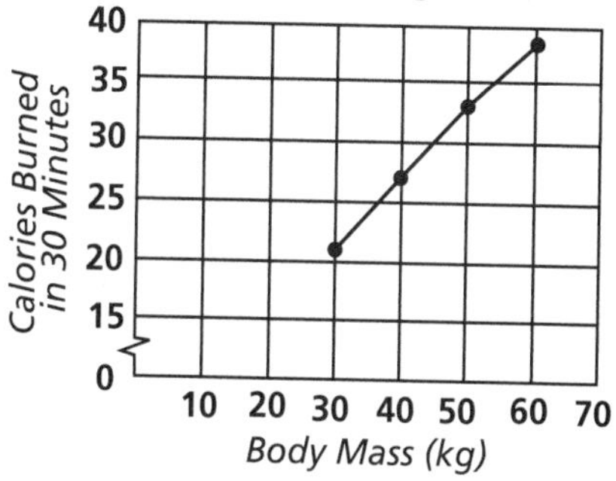

Ways Students Get to School

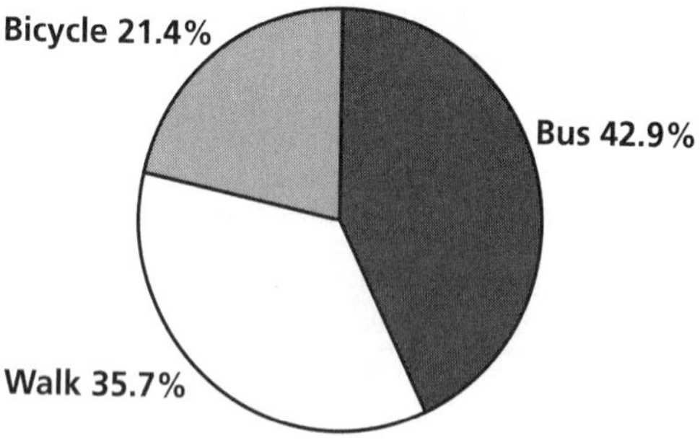

Mean, Median, and Mode

FOCUS Remind students that data from an experiment might consist of hundreds or thousands of numbers. Unless analyzed, the numbers likely will not be helpful.

TEACH Work through the process of determining mean, median, and mode using the example on page 141. Make sure students realize that these three numbers do not always equal each other. Point out that taken together, these three numbers give more information about the data than just one of the numbers alone.

Practice Answers will vary based on class data. The mean should equal the total number of minutes divided by the number of students. The median should equal the number in the middle after the data are arranged in numerical order. The mode should equal the number of minutes that is given most frequently.

Probability

FOCUS Show students a coin. **Q:** What is the chance that I will get tails when I flip the coin? **A:** Some students might know that there is a 1 in 2, or 50 percent, chance of getting tails.

TEACH Set up a bag of marbles like the one in the example on page 141. Allow students to practice determining the probabilities of picking marbles of different colors. Then, encourage them to actually pick marbles and compare their actual results with those results predicted by probability.

Practice $P(A) = 2$ sides with $\frac{A}{6}$ sides total

$P = \frac{2}{6}$, or $\frac{1}{3}$, or 33%

Area

FOCUS Ask: **Q:** Who knows what area is? **A:** Area is equal to the number of square units needed to cover a certain shape or object. On the board, write the formulas for the area of a rectangle and a circle.

TEACH Give students various objects of different shapes. Have them measure each object and determine its area based on the measurements. Point out that the units of the answer are squared because they are multiplied together. If students are interested, you might also explain that π is equal to the ratio of the circumference of a circle to its diameter. For circles of all sizes, π is approximately equal to the number 3.14, or $\frac{22}{7}$.

Practice The area of the circle is equal to $21 \text{ m} \times 21 \text{ m} \times \frac{22}{7}$, or 1,386 m^2.

Circumference

FOCUS Draw a circle on the board. Then trace the outline with your finger and explain that this is the circumference of the circle, or the distance around it.

TEACH Show students that the radius is equal to the distance from the center of the circle to any point on it. Point out that the diameter of a circle is equal to two times the radius. Give students paper circles of various sizes, and have them calculate the circumference of each.

Practice The circumference is equal to $2 \times 28 \text{ m} \times \frac{22}{7}$, or 176 m.

Volume

FOCUS Fill a beaker with 100 milliliters of water. **Q:** What is the volume of water? **A:** 100 milliliters Explain that volume is the amount of space that something takes up. Then point out that one milliliter is equal to one cubic centimeter (cm^3).

TEACH Write on the board the formulas for calculating the volumes of a rectangle and a cylinder. Point out that volume is equal to the area of an object multiplied by its height. Then measure the beaker to show students the relationship between liquid volume (100 milliliters) and the number of cubic units it contains (100 cubic centimeters).

Practice The volume of the object is $17 \text{ cm} \times 11 \text{ cm} \times 6 \text{ cm}$, or 1,122 cm^3.

Reference Section

Fractions

FOCUS Draw a circle on the board and divide it into eight equal sections. Shade in one section. Explain that one out of eight, or one eighth, of the sections is shaded. Also use the circle to show that four eighths is the same as one half.

TEACH Remind students that when you add and subtract, the denominators of the two fractions must be the same. Review how to find the least common denominator. Remind students that when you multiply and divide, the denominators don't have to be the same.

Practice $\frac{3}{7} \div \frac{4}{5} = \frac{3}{7} \times \frac{5}{4} = \frac{15}{28}$

Decimals

FOCUS Write the number 129.835 on the board. **Q:** What number is in the ones position? **A:** 9 **Q:** The tenths position? **A:** 8 **Q:** The hundredths position? **A:** 3 Make sure students know that 0.8 is equal to $\frac{8}{10}$ and 0.03 is equal to $\frac{3}{100}$.

TEACH Use the examples in the book to review addition, subtraction, multiplication, and division with decimals. Also show students how a fraction is converted to a decimal by dividing the numerator by the denominator.

Practice $6.21 \times 8.5 = 52.785$

Ratio and Proportion

FOCUS Differentiate a ratio from a fraction. Remind students that a fraction tells how many parts of the whole. A ratio compares two different numbers. For examble, a class has 12 girls and 10 boys. The fraction of girls in the class is $\frac{12}{22}$, or $\frac{6}{11}$. The ratio of boys to girls in the class is 10 to 12, or $\frac{5}{6}$.

TEACH Use the example in the book to explain how to use a proportion to find an unknown quantity. Provide students with additional practice problems, if needed.

Practice

$$6 \times 49 = 7x$$
$$294 = 7x$$
$$294 \div 7 = x$$
$$x = 42$$

Percentage

FOCUS On the board, write $50\% = \frac{50}{100}$. Explain that a percentage is a ratio that compares a number to 100.

TEACH Point out that when calculating percentages, you are usually using numbers other than 100. In this case, you set up a proportion. Go over the example in the book. Emphasize that the number representing the total goes on the bottom of the ratio, as does the 100%.

Practice Students should set up the proportion $\frac{42 \text{ marbles}}{300 \text{ marbles}} = \frac{x\%}{100\%}$

$$42 \times 100 = 300x$$
$$4200 = 300x$$
$$4200 \div 300 = 14\%$$

Significant Figures

FOCUS Measure the length of a paper clip using two different rulers. Use one ruler that is less precise than the other. Compare the two measurements. **Q:** Which measurement is more precise? **A:** The ruler with the smallest units will give a more precise measurement.

TEACH Give students the opportunity to take measurements of an object using tools with different precision. Encourage students to add and subtract their measurements, making sure that they round the answers to reflect the precision of the instruments. Go over the example for significant digits. **Q:** How many significant digits are in the number 324,000? **A:** three **Q:** In the number 5,901? **A:** four **Q:** In the number 0.706? **A:** three

Practice 26.4 m + 8.37 m = 34.77 m
This answer should be rounded to 34.8 m because the least precise measurement has only one digit after the decimal. This number is rounded up to 8 because the last digit is more than 5.

Scientific Notation

FOCUS Write a very large number on the board, such as 100 million, using all the zeros. Then, write the number using scientific notation. **Q:** Why do you think scientists prefer to write very large numbers using scientific notation? **A:** Possible answers include that it is easier to do calculations, convert units, and make comparisons with other numbers.

TEACH Go over the examples, and ask: **Q:** In the second example, which numbers are the factors? **A:** 5.8 and 10^7 **Q:** Which number is the exponent? **A:** 7 Explain that very small numbers have a negative exponent because the decimal point is moved to the right to produce the first factor. For example, 0.00000628 is equal to 6.28×10^{-6}.

Practice $6{,}590{,}000 = 6.59 \times 10^6$

Reading Comprehension Skills SE pp. 146–148

Using Prior Knowledge

FOCUS Explain to students that using prior knowledge helps connect what they already know to what they are about to read.

TEACH Point out that prior knowledge might not be accurate because memories have faded or perspectives have changed. Encourage students to ask questions to resolve discrepancies between their prior knowledge and what they have learned.

Asking Questions

FOCUS Demonstrate how to change a text heading into a question.

TEACH Encourage students to use this skill for the next section they read. Instruct them to turn the text headings into questions. Challenge students to write at least four *what, how, why, who, when,* or *where* questions. Then, have students evaluate the skill. **Q:** Did asking questions about the text help you focus on the reading and remember what you read? **A:** Encourage honesty. If this reading skill didn't help, challenge students to assess why not.

Previewing Visuals

FOCUS Explain to students that looking at the visuals before reading will help them activate prior knowledge and predict what they are about to read.

TEACH Assign a section for students to preview the visuals. First, instruct them to write a sentence describing what the section will be about. Then, encourage them to write one or two questions for each visual to give purpose to their reading. Also have them list any prior knowledge about the subject.

Outlining

FOCUS Explain that using an outline helps organize information by main topic, subtopic, and details.

TEACH Choose a section in the book, and demonstrate how to make an outline for it. Make sure students understand the structure of the outline by asking: Is this a topic or a subtopic? Where does this information go in the outline? Would I write this heading next to a Roman numeral or a capital letter? Answers depend on the section students are outlining. Also show them how to indent and add details to the outline using numerals and lowercase letters.

Identifying Main Ideas

FOCUS Explain that identifying main ideas and details helps sort the facts from the information into groups. Each group can have a main topic, subtopics, and details.

TEACH Tell students that paragraphs are often written so that the main idea is in the first sentence, in the second sentence, or in the last sentence. Assign students a page in the text. Instruct them to write the main idea for each paragraph on that page. If students have difficulty finding the main idea, suggest that they list all of the ideas given in the paragraph, and then choose the idea that is big enough to include all the others.

Comparing and Contrasting

FOCUS Explain that comparing and contrasting information shows how concepts, facts, and events are similar or different.

TEACH Point out that Venn diagrams work best when students are comparing only two things. To compare more than two things, students should use a compare/contrast table. Have students make a Venn diagram or compare/contrast table using two or more different sports or other activities, such as playing musical instruments. Emphasize that students should select characteristics that highlight the similarities and differences in the activities.

Identifying Supporting Evidence

FOCUS Explain to students that identifying the supporting evidence will help them to understand the relationship between the facts and a hypothesis.

TEACH Remind students that a hypothesis is neither right nor wrong, but it is either supported or not supported by the evidence from testing or observation. If evidence is found that does not support a hypothesis, the hypothesis can be changed to accommodate the new evidence, or it can be dropped.

Sequencing

FOCUS Tell students that organizing information from beginning to end will help them understand a step-by-step process.

TEACH Encourage students to create a flowchart to show the things they did this morning to get ready for school. Remind students that a flowchart should show the correct order in which events occur.

Then explain that a cycle diagram shows a sequence of events that is continuous. Point out the cycle diagram that shows the seasons. **Q:** Why is a cycle diagram used instead of a flowchart to show the sequence of the seasons? **A:** A cycle diagram shows that the sequence is continuous, not just a series of events. Challenge students to make a sequence diagram for a section of the text. Have them explain why they chose either a cycle diagram or a flowchart. Remind them to include at least four steps in the sequence.

Relating Cause and Effect

FOCUS Explain to students that a cause is the reason for what happens. The effect is what happens in response to the cause. Relating cause and effect helps students connect the reason for what happens to what happens as a result.

TEACH Emphasize that not all events that occur together have a cause-and-effect relationship. For example, tell students that you went to the grocery store and your car stalled. **Q:** Is there a cause-and-effect relationship in this situation? Explain. **A:** No. Going to the grocery store could not cause a car to stall.

Concept Mapping

FOCUS Elicit from students how a map shows the relationship of one geographic area to another. Connect this idea to how a concept map shows the relationship between terms and concepts.

TEACH Challenge students to make a concept map with at least three levels of concepts to organize information about types of transportation. Students should start with the phrase *Types of Transportation* at the top of the concept map. After that point, their concepts may vary. (For example, some students might place *Private Transportation* and *Public Transportation* at the next level, while other students might choose *human-powered* and *gas-powered*.) Make sure students connect the concepts with linking words.

Building Vocabulary SE p. 149

Reading in a content area presents challenges different from those encountered in fiction. Science texts often have new vocabulary and unfamiliar concepts, which place greater emphasis on inferential reasoning. Students who can apply vocabulary strategies will be more successful in reading and understanding a science textbook. Challenge students to use Greek and Latin word origins and the meanings of prefixes and suffixes to learn the Key Terms in each section.

Word Origins

FOCUS Explain that word origins describe the older, foreign words that many modern English words have come from. Many science words come from Greek and Latin.

TEACH Tell students that most dictionaries give the word origin just before the definition. Choose a section in the text that has a Key Term with a Greek or Latin word origin. Encourage students to learn the meaning of the root word. **Q:** How does knowing the word origin help you remember the meaning of the Key Term? **A:** Answers will vary, but the meaning of the Latin or Greek root should provide a clue to the definition of the Key Term. **Q:** What other words do you know that come from the same word origin? **A:** Students may mention other words related to the Key Term. Challenge students to use word origins to figure out the meanings of unfamiliar words as they read. Students should confirm their definitions as necessary by checking a dictionary.

Prefixes

FOCUS Tell students that learning the meaning of common prefixes can help them determine the meaning of words they don't recognize. They will also increase their vocabulary.

TEACH Remind students that a prefix is a word part that is added at the beginning of a root word to change its meaning. List some of the familiar prefixes and meanings, such as *de-* and *re-,* on the board. **Q:** What words do you know that use these same prefixes? **A:** Students should list at least two words for each prefix. **Q:** How does the prefix affect the meaning of the root word? **A:** Students should explain how the prefix changes the meaning. Challenge students to learn the meaning of common prefixes and to use the skill to increase their vocabulary.

Suffixes

FOCUS Explain to students that learning the meanings of common suffixes and recognizing them in words are two effective strategies for learning word meanings and building vocabulary.

TEACH Remind students that a suffix is added to the end of a word to change its meaning. In addition, students can use suffixes to discover the part of speech of an unfamiliar word. On the board, draw a four-column chart. Label the columns Noun, Verb, Adjective, and Adverb. Choose a Key Term that has a familiar base word, such as *tension.* **Q:** What are the noun, verb, adjective, and adverb forms of this word? **A:** Students should give all possible answers, which may include only two forms of the word. **Q:** What endings signal that the word is a noun, adjective, or adverb? **A:** Students should list the suffixes. Challenge students to learn the meanings of suffixes and to use them to decode new words.

Laboratory Safety SE pp. 150–151

Laboratory safety is an essential element of a successful science class. Students need to understand exactly what is safe and unsafe behavior and what is the rationale behind each safety rule.

General Precautions

- Post safety rules in the classroom, and review them regularly with students before beginning every science activity.
- Familiarize yourself with the safety procedures for each activity before introducing it to your students.
- For open-ended activities, have students submit their procedures or design plans in writing and check them for safety considerations.
- Always act as an exemplary role model by displaying safe behavior.
- Know how to use safety equipment, such as fire extinguishers and fire blankets, and always have equipment accessible.
- Have students practice leaving the classroom quickly and orderly to prepare them for emergencies.
- Explain to students how to use the intercom or other available means of communication to get help during an emergency.
- Never leave students unattended while they are engaged in science activities.
- Provide enough space for students to safely carry out science activities.
- Instruct students to report all accidents and injuries to you immediately.

End-of-Experiment Rules

- Always have students use warm water and soap for washing their hands.

Heating and Fire Safety

- No flammable substances should be in use around hot plates, light bulbs, or open flames.
- Test tubes should be heated only in water baths.
- Students should be permitted to strike matches to light candles or burners only with strict supervision. When possible, you should light the flames, especially when working with younger students.
- Be sure to have proper ventilation when fumes are produced during a procedure.
- All electrical equipment used in the lab should have GFI (Ground Fault Interrupter) switches.

Using Glassware Safely

- Use plastic containers, graduated cylinders, and beakers whenever possible. If using glass, students should wear safety goggles.
- Use only nonmercury thermometers with anti-roll protectors.

Using Chemicals Safely

- When students use both chemicals and microscopes in one activity, microscopes should be in a separate part of the room from the chemicals so that when students remove their goggles to use the microscopes, their eyes are not at risk.

Name ______________ Class ________ Date ____________ M T W T F

LESSON PLAN 1-1 Using Science to Solve Crimes

TIME
3–4 periods
1½–2 blocks

OBJECTIVES

1.1.1 Identify inquiry skills used to solve crimes.

1.1.2 Explain the importance of teamwork in solving crimes.

1.1.3 Compare methods used to solve crimes today with those used in the past.

KEY TERMS

- burglary • forensic science • observing
- evidence • inferring • predicting
- hypothesis • crime scene investigator
- medical examiner • autopsy • density

LOCAL STANDARDS

Preteach

Build Background Knowledge

THE FIVE SENSES Have students describe how each sense can be used to make observations.

Discover Activity: What Do You Know About Solving Crimes?

RESOURCES

- Vocabulary Worksheet

Instruct

Science at a Crime Scene Explain that the success of an investigation depends on the quality of the observations made at a crime scene. Have students practice making observations and distinguishing observations from inferences.

Teamwork at a Crime Scene Discuss the roles of professionals who come to a crime scene. Have students devise questions for a dispatcher to ask a 9-1-1 caller to determine who should be sent to the caller's location.

Forensic Science Methods Compare the method Archimedes used to solve a crime with the methods used by modern forensic scientists. Demonstrate how to measure density.

Skills Lab: Who Stole Dave's MP3 Player?

RESOURCES

- Reading and Note Taking Guide 1-1
- Skills Lab Worksheet
- Video Viewing Guide 1
- Video: Clues From a Murder
- Video: The Mysterious Ice Man

Assess

REVIEWING KEY CONCEPTS Have students use their concept map of Key Terms to help them answer the questions.

RETEACH Have students provide examples of how the skills listed in Figure 3 are used in everyday life.

PERFORMANCE ASSESSMENT Have students identify the object in a sealed container or explain how Archimedes used inquiry skills to solve the case of the golden crown.

Name ______________________ Class ___________ Date ________________ M T W T F

LESSON PLAN 1-2 Securing and Recording a Crime Scene

TIME
2–3 periods
1–1½ blocks

OBJECTIVES

1.2.1 Describe how to secure a crime scene.

1.2.2 Identify methods investigators use to record a crime scene.

KEY TERMS

• sketch • scale • communicating

LOCAL STANDARDS

Preteach

Build Background Knowledge

CONTROLLING ENTRY Elicit experiences students have had controlling entry to a space.

Discover Activity: How Many Footsteps?

RESOURCES

- Vocabulary Worksheet

Instruct

Securing a Crime Scene Use the Sherlock Holmes quotation to introduce the concept of securing a crime scene. Ask students to suggest ways to secure different crime scenes. Have groups of students design a system for tracking visitors to a crime scene.

Recording a Crime Scene Discuss reasons for recording a crime scene and the methods used—photographs, videos, sketches, scale drawings, written notes, and recorded notes. Use floor plan maps at malls as an analogy for crime scene sketches. Have students select the essential information for a sketch showing a driving route between locations in the community.

Forensics & Earth Science: Mapping Crime

RESOURCES

- Reading and Note Taking Guide 1-2
- Laboratory Investigation 1: Recording a Crime Scene
- SciLinks: longitude

Assess

REVIEWING KEY CONCEPTS Have students use their graphic organizer to help them answer the questions.

RETEACH Discuss the benefits and drawbacks of each method for recording a crime scene.

PERFORMANCE ASSESSMENT Have students write instructions for one of the tasks a CSI must do while recording a crime scene.

Name ______________________ Class ___________ Date _______________ M T W T F

LESSON PLAN 1-3 Types of Evidence

TIME
2–3 periods
1–1½ blocks

OBJECTIVES

1.3.1 Describe the benefits and drawbacks of direct evidence.

1.3.2 Compare the methods used to help witnesses identify suspects.

1.3.3 Explain why physical evidence is key to solving crimes.

KEY TERMS

- eyewitness
- direct evidence
- modus operandi
- surveillance camera
- physical evidence

LOCAL STANDARDS

Preteach

Build Background Knowledge

ARE OBSERVATIONS RELIABLE? Use what happens when a magician distracts an audience to explain why an eyewitness could have trouble making accurate observations.

Discover Activity: Who Was That Person?

RESOURCES

- Vocabulary Worksheet

Instruct

Direct Evidence Use observations of detailed photographs to demonstrate some factors that affect recall. Do a storytelling activity to explain why hearsay evidence isn't accepted in court.

Using Lineups and Mug Shots Discuss when police use lineups and mug shots, and how they control variables to ensure that the process is fair.

Picturing a Criminal Discuss how a forensic artist uses interviews to produce a sketch of a suspect and have students practice the process with a partner.

Physical Evidence Discuss Locard's Principle and have students apply it to various situations.

RESOURCES

- Reading and Note Taking Guide 1-3
- Laboratory Investigation 2: Making Faces
- Video Viewing Guide 1
- Video: Interviewing Witnesses

Assess

REVIEWING KEY CONCEPTS Have students use their graphic organizer to help them answer the questions.

RETEACH Ask students to identify the concept being illustrated in each figure.

PERFORMANCE ASSESSMENT Have students contrast making observations in a lab with making observations at a crime scene or have them summarize ways witnesses can identify a suspect.

Name ______________________ Class __________ Date ________________ M T W T F

LESSON PLAN 1-4 Collecting Physical Evidence

TIME
2 periods
1 block

OBJECTIVES

1.4.1 Identify factors investigators consider before searching a crime scene.

1.4.2 Describe methods investigators use to ensure that the evidence found at a crime scene can be used in court.

1.4.3 Explain how investigators protect themselves at a crime scene.

KEY TERMS
• contamination • chain of custody

LOCAL STANDARDS

Preteach

Build Background Knowledge

COLLECTING EVIDENCE Use how students package and label the items they find during a scavenger hunt to introduce the importance of packaging and labeling evidence.

Discover Activity: **How Would You Collect This Evidence?**

RESOURCES

- Vocabulary Worksheet

Instruct

Organizing a Search Compare the strategies students use for finding a lost item with the search patterns used by investigators. Stress that a search must be organized so that evidence will not be overlooked. Then have students search for a hidden item.

Keeping Evidence Useful Compare the packing of objects when a person moves to the packaging of crime scene evidence, and tracking data from a shipped package to a chain of custody.

Protecting the Investigators Relate the safety guidelines used by investigators at a crime scene to the safety rules students must follow during lab activities.

RESOURCES

- Reading and Note Taking Guide 1-4
- Laboratory Investigation 3: Collecting Physical Evidence
- SciLinks: careers in science

Assess

REVIEWING KEY CONCEPTS Have students use their graphic organizer to help them answer the questions.

RETEACH Have students use Figure 24 to explain why it is important to establish a chain of custody.

PERFORMANCE ASSESSMENT Have teams of students select equipment to collect the evidence at their assigned lab station. Have intermediate English learners label the collected evidence.

RESOURCES

- Chapter 1 Test

Name ____________________ Class __________ Date ______________ M T W T F

LESSON PLAN 2-1 Prints

TIME
3–4 periods
1½–2 blocks

OBJECTIVES

2.1.1 Describe the kinds of prints investigators look for at a crime scene.

2.1.2 Summarize methods used to preserve and compare prints.

2.1.3 Explain why investigators need search warrants.

KEY TERMS

- print
- imprint
- impression
- skid mark
- cast
- search warrant

LOCAL STANDARDS

Preteach

Build Background Knowledge

FOOTPRINTS Discuss how scientists use the tracks left by dinosaurs to help determine their size. Explain that detectives use similar evidence left by humans to solve crimes.

Discover Activity: What's the Difference?

RESOURCES

- Vocabulary Worksheet

Instruct

Types of Prints Use the organization of furniture in a classroom to introduce the term *pattern*. Discuss how wear affects the marks left by objects with distinctive patterns. Have students make and label rubbings of tire treads.

Preserving Prints Discuss how investigators use prints and casts to preserve prints. Then have students make a cast of an object with a distinctive pattern.

Comparing Prints Use a library catalogue to introduce databases. Then discuss how print examiners use databases to compare prints.

Search Warrants Explain why police need search warrants and how they obtain warrants.

Skills Lab: Analyzing Shoe Prints

RESOURCES

- Reading and Note Taking Guide 2-1
- Skills Lab Worksheet
- Laboratory Investigation 4: Casting Suspicion
- Video Viewing Guide 2
- Video: Tire Tracks Trap Killer

Assess

REVIEWING KEY CONCEPTS Have students use their graphic organizer to help them answer the questions.

RETEACH Have students make a flowchart showing the sequence of events after the discovery of a tire tread impression.

PERFORMANCE ASSESSMENT Have students apply the correct Key Term to selected objects.

Name ______________________ Class ____________ Date ________________ M T W T F

LESSON PLAN 2-2 Trace Evidence

TIME
3–4 periods
1½–2 blocks

OBJECTIVES

2.2.1 Describe how a CSI collects trace evidence.
2.2.2 List five major types of trace evidence.
2.2.3 Explain how crime labs use technology to test trace evidence.

KEY TERMS

- trace evidence
- classifying
- concentration
- chromatography
- microscope

LOCAL STANDARDS

Preteach

Build Background Knowledge

TRACES OF EVIDENCE Use a bit of frosting from a cake as an example of trace evidence.

Discover Activity: What Clues Does Sand Contain?

RESOURCES

- Vocabulary Worksheet

Instruct

Collecting Trace Evidence Have students use the story in the text to make a list of trace evidence. Then discuss how a CSI could collect each type of evidence.

Types of Trace Evidence Have small groups of students present information about different types of trace evidence. Have students view hairs under a microscope. Use the visuals to discuss other types of trace evidence.

Using Chromatography Have students use paper chromatography to separate ink. Use Figure 14 to compare and contrast paper chromatography and gas chromatography.

Using Microscopes Discuss different types of microscopes, and explain why forensic scientists use comparison microscopes.

Forensics & Physical Science: Arson Investigations

RESOURCES

- Reading and Note Taking Guide 2-2
- Laboratory Investigation 5: Splitting Hairs
- Laboratory Investigation 6: Lipstick Tells the Tale
- Laboratory Investigation 7: A Clear-Cut Case
- SciLinks: soil types
- SciLinks: fire triangle
- Video Viewing Guide 2
- Video: Arson-Sniffing Dogs

Assess

REVIEWING KEY CONCEPTS Have students use their graphic organizer to help them answer the questions.

RETEACH Have small groups of students take turns asking the other students in the group questions about the lesson.

PERFORMANCE ASSESSMENT Have students write a paragraph explaining how investigators could use paint chips to locate a car or have them compare what scientists do to analyze hair samples and soil samples.

Name ______________________ Class ___________ Date _______________ M T W T F

LESSON PLAN 2–3 Identifying Firearms

TIME
2 periods
1 block

OBJECTIVES
2.3.1 Compare the types of evidence that investigators collect when a weapon is fired.
2.3.2 Summarize the methods used to analyze evidence from firearms.

KEY TERMS
• cartridge • rifling • gunshot residue

LOCAL STANDARDS

Preteach

Build Background Knowledge

USING PRIOR KNOWLEDGE Have students use what they have learned from books, movies, or television to predict the prints and trace evidence left by firearms.

Discover Activity: Where Does the Powder Go?

RESOURCES
- Vocabulary Worksheet

Instruct

Evidence From Firearms Use a discussion of paintball to introduce the topic of firearms evidence. Have students identify and record the purpose of selected items in Figure 16 on a copy of the illustration. Then have students relate the design and operation of a gun to the evidence that is produced when the gun is fired.

Analyzing Firearms Evidence Discuss how a firearms expert obtains and analyzes firearms evidence. Stress the need for test firings and the use of a comparison microscope.

RESOURCES
- Reading and Note Taking Guide 2-3
- Video Viewing Guide 2
- Video: Firearms Evidence

Assess

REVIEWING KEY CONCEPTS Have students use their graphic organizer to help them answer the questions.

RETEACH Use the images in Figure 18 to review the production and analysis of firearms evidence.

PERFORMANCE ASSESSMENT Have students prepare a training guide for a firearms expert.

RESOURCES
- Chapter 2 Test

Name ______________________ Class ____________ Date ________________ M T W T F

LESSON PLAN 3-1 Fingerprints

TIME
4 periods
2 blocks

OBJECTIVES

3.1.1 Distinguish patterns used to describe fingerprints.

3.1.2 Compare methods used to collect latent prints.

3.1.3 Explain how examiners analyze the prints found at a crime scene.

KEY TERMS

- ridge
- visible print
- plastic print
- latent print

LOCAL STANDARDS

Preteach

Build Background Knowledge

RIDGES Compare the ribs on a tire tread to the ridges on fingertips. Define *ridge* and discuss other examples of ridges.

Discover Activity: What Can You See on a Fingertip?

RESOURCES

- Vocabulary Worksheet

Instruct

Describing Fingerprints Use Figure 1 to discuss fingerprint patterns and the details that distinguish one fingerprint from another. Make 3-D models of the patterns for visually impaired students. Have students make and analyze their own fingerprints.

Collecting Fingerprints Explain how people leave latent prints on surfaces. Use Figure 2 to discuss some methods used to reveal and lift latent prints.

Identifying Fingerprints Discuss how examiners get prints to compare with prints collected at a crime scene. Then discuss the three levels of review done by print examiners and the role of fingerprint databases.

RESOURCES

- Reading and Note Taking Guide 3-1
- Laboratory Investigation 8: Latent Clues
- Video Viewing Guide 3
- Video: Fingerprint Evidence

Assess

REVIEWING KEY CONCEPTS Have students use their graphic organizer to help them answer the questions.

RETEACH Have students make a flowchart to show the sequence of steps from the discovery of a fingerprint to finding a match.

PERFORMANCE ASSESSMENT Have students summarize the techniques for dusting and lifting prints or have them write a paragraph comparing eliminating prints from evidence to deciding what objects to include in a crime scene sketch.

Name ______________________ Class ____________ Date ________________ M T W T F

LESSON PLAN 3-2 Evidence From Blood

TIME
3 periods
1½ blocks

OBJECTIVES
3.2.1 Describe the methods used to detect blood.
3.2.2 Explain how blood is classified.
3.2.3 Interpret patterns of bloodstains.

KEY TERMS
• hemoglobin • luminol • antibody

LOCAL STANDARDS

Preteach

Build Background Knowledge

BLOOD Discuss the composition of blood, and have students view a prepared slide of blood.

Discover Activity: What Can Blood Drops Reveal?

RESOURCES
- Vocabulary Worksheet

Instruct

Searching for Blood Discuss how a CSI can find traces of blood at a crime scene. Demonstrate a reaction that occurs when luminol is used to detect blood.

Classifying Blood Explain how marker molecules on red blood cells can be used to classify blood.

Bloodstain Patterns Use the results of the Discover Activity to introduce variables that affect the size and shape of bloodstains. Then have students use fake blood to test some of these variables.

Forensics & Life Science: Facial Reconstruction

RESOURCES
- Reading and Note Taking Guide 3-2
- Laboratory Investigation 9: Every Drop Tells a Story
- Video Viewing Guide 3
- Video: Clues From Bloodstains
- SciLinks: blood type
- SciLinks: animal symmetry

Assess

REVIEWING KEY CONCEPTS Have students use their graphic organizer to help them answer the questions.

RETEACH Use index cards with blood types and antibody types to review what happens when blood and antisera are mixed.

PERFORMANCE ASSESSMENT Present statements about blood and ask students to decide whether the statements are true.

Name ______________________ Class ___________ Date ________________ M T W T F

LESSON PLAN 3-3 DNA Evidence

TIME
4–5 periods
2–2½ blocks

OBJECTIVES

3.3.1 State the reason for DNA's value as a tool for forensic scientists.

3.3.2 Summarize the process for making a DNA profile.

3.3.3 Explain why DNA profiles are accepted as evidence.

3.3.4 Describe the uses of DNA profiles.

KEY TERMS
• DNA • protein • gene • DNA profile
• replication • probability • cold case
• endangered species

LOCAL STANDARDS

Preteach

Build Background Knowledge

CELL STRUCTURE Use a diagram of an animal cell to discuss the function of various structures in a cell.

Discover Activity: How Long Can You Make a Match?

RESOURCES
- Vocabulary Worksheet

Instruct

DNA Molecules Use Figure 8 to teach the structure of DNA. Then have students build a model of DNA.

Making a DNA Profile Discuss how scientists collect, isolate, multiply, and sort DNA. Then demonstrate how DNA can be isolated from a strawberry.

Probability Use a coin, a die, and a pack of cards to show how increasing the number of possibilities affects the probability of an event. Then use Figure 12 to apply this concept to DNA.

Uses of DNA Profiles Use cold cases as an example of how DNA is used to solve crimes. Have students research other uses.

RESOURCES
- Reading and Note Taking Guide 3-3
- Laboratory Investigation 10: The Power of DNA Evidence
- Video Viewing Guide 3
- Video: DNA to the Rescue
- SciLinks: DNA fingerprinting

Assess

REVIEWING KEY CONCEPTS Have students use their graphic organizer to help them answer the questions.

RETEACH Provide a paragraph about DNA profiles with blanks for students to fill in.

PERFORMANCE ASSESSMENT Have students use snap cubes to build a a model of a segment of DNA.

Name ____________________ Class __________ Date ______________ M T W T F

LESSON PLAN 3-4 Handwriting and Voice Identification

TIME
2 periods
1 block

OBJECTIVES
3.4.1 Identify clues used to compare writing samples.
3.4.2 Describe the methods analysts use to compare voice samples.

KEY TERMS
- voiceprint

LOCAL STANDARDS

Preteach

Build Background Knowledge

CONTENT CLUES Ask a librarian to select two age-appropriate authors who write in the same genre but have different styles. Read a passage from each author. Then ask students to decide whether they think the passages were written by the same author, and why.

Discover Activity: Can Handwriting Identify a Person?

RESOURCES
- Vocabulary Worksheet

Instruct

Handwriting Identification Ask volunteers to write their signatures on the board. Have the class look for similarities and differences among the samples.

Voice Identification Discuss traits that can be used to recognize who is speaking from a recording.

Skills Lab: Measuring Writing

RESOURCES
- Reading and Note Taking Guide 3-4
- Skills Lab Worksheet
- Video Viewing Guide 3
- Video: Voice Stress Analysis

Assess

REVIEWING KEY CONCEPTS Have students use their graphic organizer to help them answer the questions.

RETEACH Compare the process of analyzing a voiceprint with handwriting analysis.

PERFORMANCE ASSESSMENT Have students working in small groups each copy two passages you have written on the board onto index cards. Have the groups shuffle the cards and exchange them with another group. The groups should then pair up the cards in their stack by writer.

RESOURCES
- Chapter 3 Test

Name ____________________ Class __________ Date ______________ M T W T F

LESSON PLAN 4-1 From Arrest to Trial

TIME
3 periods
1½ blocks

OBJECTIVES
4.1.1 Explain how a person's rights are protected before, during, and after an arrest.
4.1.2 Classify crimes as felonies or misdemeanors.
4.1.3 Summarize what typically happens between an arrest and a trial.

KEY TERMS
- Bill of Rights • jury • bail • felony
- misdemeanor • probable cause • defendant
- judge • prosecutor • public defender
- plea bargain

LOCAL STANDARDS

Preteach

Build Background Knowledge

BRANCHES OF GOVERNMENT Discuss the roles of the executive, legislative, and judicial branches of government.

Discover Activity: When Is a Suspect Guilty?

RESOURCES
- Vocabulary Worksheet

Instruct

The Bill of Rights Discuss a version of the First Amendment that you have rewritten in words students will understand. Then have groups of students use information in the text and a copy of the Bill of Rights to rewrite other amendments.

Types of Crimes Classify school rules based on the possible punishments for violations. Use the classification as an analogy to the classification of crimes as misdemeanors and felonies.

Making an Arrest Have students use the examples in the text to list the observations and inferences that police use as probable cause for an arrest. Ask students to compare search warrants and arrest warrants.

Pretrial Procedures Discuss various issues that can arise at a pretrial hearing. Then use the charges listed in Figure 5 to discuss how charges may be reduced as part of a plea bargain.

RESOURCES
- Reading and Note Taking Guide 4-1
- Video Viewing Guide 4
- Video: Bill of Rights

Assess

REVIEWING KEY CONCEPTS Have students use their four-column chart titled "Bill of Rights" to help them answer the questions.

RETEACH Pretend you are a judge and ask students to help you determine what to do at a pretrial hearing.

PERFORMANCE ASSESSMENT Have students explain how a defendant's rights are protected after an arrest.

Name ______________________ Class __________ Date ______________ M T W T F

LESSON PLAN 4-2 Presenting Evidence in a Trial

TIME
3 periods
1½ blocks

OBJECTIVES

4.2.1 Compare the assigned roles of a judge, an impartial jury, and the lawyers at a criminal trial.

4.2.2 Identify ways that lawyers use exhibits in court.

4.2.3 Explain how lawyers use witnesses to present evidence.

KEY TERMS
- bailiff
- exhibit
- testimony
- cross-examination
- expert witness

LOCAL STANDARDS

Preteach

Build Background Knowledge

FICTION VS. FACT Discuss how a typical fictional trial may differ from an actual trial.

Discover Activity: What Makes a Good Juror?

RESOURCES
- Vocabulary Worksheet

Instruct

In the Courtroom Use Figure 6 to discuss the roles of the participants in a trial.

A Jury Is Chosen Discuss how a jury is selected. Then use a set of juror profiles to apply the process to the Hauptmann trial.

The Lawyers Argue the Case Explain the adversary system for presenting evidence. Compare a trial to a debate.

Visual Evidence Discuss different types of exhibits. Have students apply what they learn to the case of the stolen dog.

Oral Evidence Compare direct examination and cross-examination. Have students apply the need to ask questions in a logical order to the example of an expert witness on DNA.

Skills Lab: Making a Scale Model

Forensics & Technology: Modeling a Crime Scene

RESOURCES
- Reading and Note Taking Guide 4-2
- Skills Lab Worksheet
- Laboratory Investigation 11: Expert Opinions
- Video Viewing Guide 4
- Video: Trial by Jury
- Video: Virtual Crime Scenes
- SciLinks: lasers

Assess

REVIEWING KEY CONCEPTS Have students use their graphic organizer to help them answer the questions.

RETEACH Have students make a chart to show what they learned about judges, juries, lawyers, and witnesses.

PERFORMANCE ASSESSMENT Have students compare the roles of a prosecutor and defense lawyer, or describe jury selection.

Name ______________ Class __________ Date ______________ M T W T F

LESSON PLAN 4-3 The Final Stages of a Trial

TIME
2 periods
1 block

OBJECTIVES

4.3.1 Describe the process a jury uses to reach a verdict.

4.3.2 State what happens when a person is found guilty.

KEY TERMS

- verdict
- foreperson
- probation
- appeal

LOCAL STANDARDS

Preteach

Build Background Knowledge

REACHING CONSENSUS Discuss methods people use to reach an agreement.

Discover Activity: Is the Evidence Persuasive?

RESOURCES

- Vocabulary Worksheet

Instruct

The Case Goes to the Jury Explain the difference between a debate and a deliberation.

Sentences and Appeals Discuss how a judge decides on a sentence and what factors affect the judge's decision. Present scenarios that include those factors and ask students to propose an appropriate sentence.

RESOURCES

- Reading and Note Taking Guide 4-3

Assess

REVIEWING KEY CONCEPTS Have students use their graphic organizer to help them answer the questions.

RETEACH Have students identify a main idea and supporting details for the paragraphs below each blue heading.

PERFORMANCE ASSESSMENT Have students write instructions for a jury or make a flowchart showing the sequence of events from closing arguments to a verdict being read.

RESOURCES

- Chapter 4 Test
- Unit Test